JN092601

日経サイエンスで鍛える科学英語

心理学 編

Scientific English with
SCIENTIFIC AMERICAN®/
NIKKEI SCIENCE

鈴木光太郎［監修］
日経サイエンス編集部［編］

日経サイエンス社

まえがき

本書は『日経サイエンスで鍛える科学英語』シリーズの6冊目，心理学編である。月刊科学誌 SCIENTIFIC AMERICAN（日本版は「日経サイエンス」）に掲載された心理学関連の記事のなかから17編を厳選し，原文と訳文を対照させて示してある。最近は機械翻訳やAI翻訳によって，原文を直接読む機会が少なくなりつつあるが，ぜひ原文で記事を読むことに挑戦していただきたい。

SCIENTIFIC AMERICAN は，言うまでもなく商業誌。そこに掲載される article（記事）は，学術専門誌の論文とは異なり，一般の読者もある程度の知識があれば読んでわかるように書かれている。特徴は，もちろんコンパクトでわかりやすい解説にあるが，それに加えて，読者を惹きつけるタイトルと，引き込まれるような冒頭の話の展開（いわゆる「つかみ」）も大きな特徴だ。本書に掲載してあるのは，冒頭の「つかみ」の部分を含んだ記事の前半部分である（短めの1編については全文を掲載した）。この導入部分を読みこなせれば，あとはそう問題なく読み通せるはずである。

本書は5つのセクションから構成してある。最初にとりあげるのは，感覚間の相互作用，匂いと記憶の関係，眠りと記憶，人工意識といった「感覚と意識」をめぐるトピックである。次のセクションでは，所有物への愛着，反抗期の若者の脳，赤ちゃんの言語発達といった「心の発達」の問題を，3番目のセクションでは，子育て支援と子どもの脳の発達，プラセボ効果と脳，子どもの認知研究とAI，神経回路網と知性といった「心と脳」の問題をあつかう。続いて「創造する心」では，コロナ禍での睡眠や夢の変化，半覚醒状態とひらめき，天才の創造性といった問題を，最終セクション「心と社会」では，ヒト特有の協力行動，SNSと認知バイアス，コロナ禍でのモラルインジャリーの問題をとりあげる。ただ，記事はそれぞれ独立しているので，セクションや順番にこだわらずに，興味のある記事から読み始めていただいてまったく問題ない。

各記事の表題ページには，最初に「KEY CONCEPTS」として記事の要点を示してある（これは日本語のみの掲載）。英文本文の右側には，語注「Vocabulary」を併記した。とくに大学や大学院入試の英文読解の参考書として本書を使用される方には，読解の助けとして有効にお使いいただけると思う。また，「この記事の読み方」では，各記事のポイントや用語について簡単に解説してある。

収録した記事は，佳境に入るところで終わっている場合も多い。さらに続きを読んでみたい方は，SCIENTIFIC AMERICANの原文にあたるか，訳文でよければ，本書末尾の2編を除く15編が別冊日経サイエンス255『新版 意識と感覚の脳科学』と同259『新版 認知科学で探る心の成長と発達』に収められているので，そちらを参照いただきたい。

なお，「日経サイエンス」の訳文は，読みやすくするために逐語訳はしていない。原文にはない内容を補足したり，部分的に順序を入れ替えたり，論旨を損なわない範囲で省略している場合がある。和訳の試験で求められるような逐語訳ではないことをお断りしておく。

本誌「日経サイエンス」のウェブサイト（https://www.nikkei-science.com）には「英語で読む日経サイエンス」というページがある。各号の主要記事から毎月1～2本について，冒頭の数パラグラフの原文・訳文を対照させて掲載している。また本誌上でも，「今月の科学英語」を連載している。これらもあわせてご利用いただければ幸いである。

鈴木光太郎

日経サイエンスで鍛える科学英語［心理学編］　目次

装丁：八十島博明
カバーイラスト：中村知史
編集協力：株式会社アイディ
DTP：GRID

凡例

※翻訳記事では，よりわかりやすく読みやすい文章にするため，内容を補強あるいは省略するなどの変更を加えている場合があり，必ずしも英文記事の逐語訳とはなっていない。また，改行位置の変更など日経サイエンスの誌面掲載時とは異なる文章になっている場合がある。

※各記事の掲載時期を，記事冒頭ページの下部に SCIENTIFIC AMERICAN および日経サイエンスの掲載号で示した。

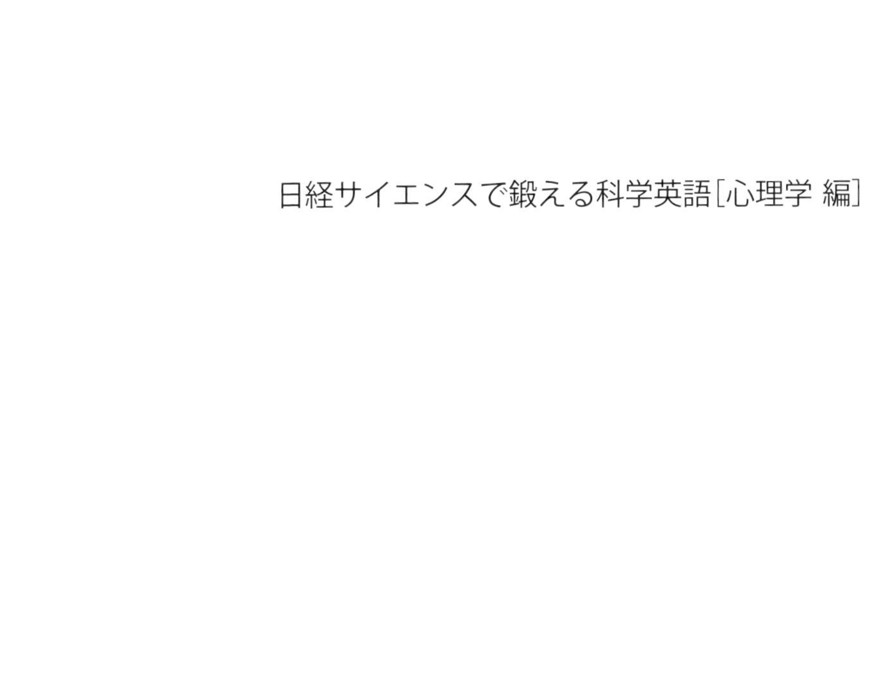

日経サイエンスで鍛える科学英語［心理学 編］

感覚と意識

1

A Confederacy of Senses

助け合う感覚

Smells Like Old Times

匂いと記憶の深い関係

Perchance to Prune

眠りが刈り込む余計な記憶

Proust among the Machines

機械は意識を持ちうるか

A Confederacy of Senses

助け合う感覚

L. D. ローゼンブラム
（米カリフォルニア大学リバーサイド校）

視覚や聴覚などまるで異なるように思える感覚が
想像以上に深く絡み合っていることがわかった
視覚や触覚の影響で聞こえ方が大きく変わる

KEY CONCEPTS

五感を融合するよう進化した脳

- ■視覚や聴覚，嗅覚，味覚，触覚など，種類の異なる感覚ごとに，それを専門に処理する領域が脳に存在していると考えられてきた。さまざまな工具を収めたキャンピングナイフのようなものとみる考え方だ。
- ■しかし過去30年の心理学や神経科学の研究によって，脳は実は非常に多感覚の器官であることが明らかになった。脳はさまざまな感覚情報を常に融合している。
- ■この“多感覚革命”ともいうべき転換は脳の機能に対する理解を大きく変えただけでなく，視聴覚障害者を助ける新たな方法を示している。音声認識ソフトウエアの改良にも役立っている。

日経サイエンス 2013年4月号，SCIENTIFIC AMERICAN January 2013

In the late 1970s the FBI hired Sue Thomas, along with eight other deaf individuals, to analyze fingerprint patterns. Deaf people, the agency reasoned, might have an easier time staying focused during the notoriously meticulous task. From the first day, however, Thomas found the job unbearably monotonous. She complained to her superiors so often that she was prepared to walk away unemployed when her boss summoned her to a meeting with other agents in his office.

But Thomas was not fired—she was, in a sense, promoted. The agents showed her a silent video of two criminal suspects conversing and asked her to decipher their conversation.

In their own interactions with Thomas, the agents had noticed how deftly she read their lips. As her co-workers anticipated, Thomas easily interpreted the suspects' dialogue, which implicated them in an illegal gambling ring. So began Thomas's career as the FBI's first deaf lipreading expert.

A lifetime's dependence on lipreading to communicate had honed Thomas's skill, but we all rely on the same talent more than we know. In fact, our ability to understand speech is diminished if we cannot see the lips of the speaker, especially in a noisy environment or when the speaker has a thick accent that is foreign to us. Learning to perceive speech with our eyes, as well as our ears, is an important part of typical speech development; as a consequence, blind infants—who cannot see the mouths of speakers around them—often take longer than average to learn certain aspects of speech. We simply cannot help but integrate the words we see on another's lips with the words we hear. In recent years research on multisensory speech perception has helped bring about a revolution in our understanding of how the brain organizes the information it receives from our many different senses.

Vocabulary

［タイトル］ **confederacy** 同盟，徒党，共謀
▶この記事の読み方

hire 雇う
deaf 耳の聞こえない
reason 推論する
stay focused 集中力を保つ
notoriously 言わずと知れた
meticulous 綿密な，きめ細かな
unbearably 耐えがたいほど
monotonous 単調な
superior 上司
prepared 覚悟する
walk away unemployed 解雇を言い渡される
summon 呼び出す
agent 捜査員

fired クビになる
promoted 昇進する，昇格する
suspect 容疑者
converse 会話をする
decipher 解読する，読み解く

interaction やりとり
deftly 巧みに
interprete 解釈する，解読する
implicate 示唆する
gambling ring 賭博組織
lipreading 読唇（術）
▶この記事の読み方

dependence 依存
hone 磨く
speech 発話，発話内容
diminished 減じる
accent なまり
foreign 聞き慣れない
perceive 知覚する
as well as ~ ～だけでなく
as a consequence 結果として
cannot help but ～せずにはいられない
multisensory（speech）perception（会話の）多感覚知覚
▶この記事の読み方
bring about もたらす

Neuroscientists and psychologists have largely abandoned early ideas of the brain as a Swiss Army knife, in which many distinct regions are dedicated to different senses. Instead scientists now think that the brain has evolved to encourage as much cross talk as possible between the senses—that the brain's sensory regions are physically intertwined.

Our senses are always eavesdropping on one another and sticking their noses in one another's business. Although the visual cortex is primarily concerned with vision, for example, it is perfectly capable of interpreting other sensory information as well. Within 90 minutes of being blindfolded, a seeing person becomes extra sensitive to touch via the visual cortex; likewise, brain scans have shown that blind people's visual cortices rewire themselves for hearing. When we snack on potato chips, the crispness of our crunching partially determines how good we think the chips taste—and researchers can bias the results of taste tests by tweaking what people hear. Where we look when we stand still, and what we see, shapes our whole body posture. Put simply, research in the past 15 years demonstrates that no sense works alone. The multisensory revolution is also suggesting new ways to improve devices for the blind and deaf, such as cochlear implants.

Silent Syllables

One of the earliest and most robust examples of multisensory perception is known as the McGurk effect, first reported by Harry McGurk and John MacDonald in 1976. If you watch a video clip of someone silently and repeatedly mouthing the syllable "ga" while you listen to a recording of the same person speaking the syllable "ba," you will hear them pronouncing "da." The silent "ga" syllables change your perception of the audible "ba" syllables because the brain integrates what the body hears and sees. The McGurk effect works in all languages and continues to work even if you have been studying it for 25 years—I can

Vocabulary

neuroscientist 神経科学者
distinct はっきり異なる
region 領域
dedicated to ～を専門に扱う
instead そうではなく
evolve 進化する
sensory region 感覚領域
intertwined 絡み合っている

eavesdrop 傍受する
stick one's nose in ～に口出しをする, ちょっかいを出す
visual cortex 視覚野, 視覚皮質
as well ～も, 同様に
blindfold 目隠しをする
seeing person 目の見える人
brain scan 脳画像
cortices cortexの複数形
hearing 聴覚
snack on つまむ
crispness パリパリする音
crunch かみ砕く
bias 偏らせる
tweak 手を加える
stand still じっと立つ
posture 姿勢
put simply 簡単に言えば, 要は
multisensory revolution 多感覚革命
▶この記事の読み方
cochlear implant 人工内耳

syllable 音節
▶この記事の読み方
robust 確固とした
McGurk effect マガーク効果
▶この記事の読み方
mouth 口の形だけで言う
pronounce 発音する
perception 知覚
audible 聞こえる
work 生じる
vouch 請け合う

vouch for that myself.

The speech you hear is also influenced by the speech you feel. In 1991 Carol Fowler, then at Dartmouth College, and her colleagues asked naive volunteers to try something called the Tadoma technique, in which you interpret someone's speech by placing your fingers on their lips, cheek and neck. Before cochlear implants, many deaf-blind individuals (including Helen Keller) relied on Tadoma. The syllables the volunteers felt changed how they interpreted syllables coming from nearby loudspeakers.

In 1997 Gemma Calvert, then at the University of Oxford, mapped the areas of the brain that are most active during lipreading. Volunteers with no formal lipreading experience silently lipread a face that slowly articulated the numbers one through nine. Calvert and her colleagues found that lipreading fired up the auditory cortex—the region of the brain that processes sounds—as well as related brain regions known to be active when someone hears speech. This was one of the first demonstrations of cross-sensory influences on an area of the brain thought to be dedicated to a single sense. More recent studies have contributed further evidence of sensory synthesis. For example, scientists now know that the auditory brain stem responds to aspects of seen speech, whereas before they thought it was involved only in more rudimentary processing of sounds. Neuroimaging studies have shown that during the McGurk effect—hearing "da" even though the recorded sound is "ba"—the brain behaves as though the syllable "da" were falling on that person's ears.

These findings suggest that the brain may give equal weight to speech gleaned from the ears, the eyes and even the skin. This is not to say that these distinct modalities provide an equal amount of information: clearly, hearing captures more articulatory detail than sight or touch. Rather the brain makes a concerted effort to consider and

Vocabulary

then 当時
colleague 共同研究者
naive 未経験の
volunteers 被験者
Tadoma technique タドマ法
deaf-blind individual 盲ろう者

map はっきり描く，明らかにする
active 活性化する
articulate 発音する
fire up 活性化させる
auditory cortex 聴覚野，聴覚皮質
demonstration 実証
cross-sensory 異種感覚間の
contribute 提供する
sensory synthesis 感覚統合 ▶この記事の読み方
auditory brain stem 聴性脳幹
involved 関わっている
rudimentary 基本的な
neuroimaging study 脳画像研究
fall on someone's ears 聞こえる，耳に入る

glean 集める
not to say that ～というのではない
modality 感覚モダリティー
articulatory 構音の
sight 視覚
concerted 協調的な

combine all the different types of speech information it receives, regardless of modality.

Vocabulary

regardless of ～に関係なく

Written All over Your Face

In other instances, distinct senses help one another process the same type of information. The specific manner in which a person speaks, for example, provides information about who they are, regardless of whether their speech is seen or heard. My colleagues and I film people speaking and manipulate the resulting videos to remove all recognizable facial features—transforming faces into patterns of glowing dots that dart and bob like fireflies where someone's cheeks and lips would have appeared. When we play the videos, our volunteers can lipread these faceless cluster of dots and recognize their friends.

specific 特有の
manipulate 加工する
facial features 顔の特徴
glowing dot 輝点
dart and bob あちこち飛び回る
firefly ホタル
cluster 集団

Simple sounds derived from speech can also clue us in to a person's identity. Robert Remez of Columbia University and his colleagues reduce normal speech recordings to sine waves that sound something like the whistles and bloops emitted by R2-D2 in Star Wars. Despite missing the typical qualities that distinguish voices such as pitch and timbre, these sine waves retain speaking-style information that allows listeners to recognize their friends. Most strikingly, volunteers can match these sine waves to glowing dot videos of the same person talking.

derived from ～に由来する
clue someone in ～に手がかりをもたらす
reduce 還元する
sine wave 正弦波
bloop 低周波の雑音
emit 発する
distinguish 区別する
pitch 音の高低
timbre 音色
retain 保持する
speaking style 話しぶり
match 対応づける

The fact that stripped-down versions of both heard and seen speech preserve similar information about speech style suggests that these distinct modes of perception are entangled in the brain. Neuroimaging research supports this connection: listening to the voice of someone familiar induces neural activity in the fusiform gyrus, an area of the human brain involved in recognizing faces.

stripped-down 簡略化した
entangled 絡み合っている
someone familiar よく知っている人
induce 誘発する
fusiform gyrus 紡錘状回

These findings inspired an even more outlandish prediction. If these forms of perception are mingled, then learning to read someone's lips should simultaneously

outlandish 風変わりな，奇抜な
mingle 混ぜ合わせる
simultaneously 同時に

improve one's ability to hear his or her spoken words. We asked volunteers with no lipreading experience to practice lipreading silent videos of someone speaking for one hour. Afterward, the volunteers listened to a set of spoken sentences played against a background of random noise. Unbeknownst to them, half the participants listened to sentences spoken by the same person they had just lipread, whereas the other half heard sentences from a different speaker. The volunteers who lipread and listened to the same person were more successful at picking out the sentences from the noise.

Vocabulary

played against a background 背景に重ねて再生される
unbeknownst それと知らせずに

1970 年代の末，FBI（米連邦捜査局）は指紋を解析する職員としてトーマス（Sue Thomas）ら 8 人の耳の聞こえない人を雇った。指紋解析は非常に細かな作業なので，耳の聞こえない人なら集中力を保ちやすいだろうと考えたからだ。しかし，トーマスは初日から，この仕事を耐えがたいほど退屈に感じた。上司に何度も不満を訴えていたので，ある日所内の会議に呼び出されたときには，解雇を言い渡されるのだろうと覚悟した。

だが，トーマスはクビにはならず，むしろある意味では昇格した。その会議で捜査員たちは 2 人の容疑者が会話している無音ビデオをトーマスに見せ，話の中身を解読するよう求めた。

捜査員たちはトーマスとの以前の会話から，彼女が読唇術に優れていることを実感していた。トーマスは期待通りに容疑者の会話をやすやすと解読し，この 2 人が違法賭博の一味らしいことが判明した。こうして，FBI 初の読唇術専門家としてのトーマスの仕事が始まった。

彼女のこの能力は，それまでコミュニケーションを読唇術に頼ってきた長い間の経験によって磨かれたものだ。しかし，自分では気づいていないかもしれないが，人はみな同様の能力に頼っている。実際，話者の唇が見えないと，発話内容を理解しにくくなる。周囲に雑音が多い場合や，話者に聞き慣れないなまりがある場合は特にそうだ。耳だけでなく目を通じて話を知覚する方法を学習することは，言語能力の発達の重要な部分をなしている。だから，生まれつき目の見えない赤ちゃん（周囲で話している人たちの口元を見ることができない乳児）は平均よりも会話能力の習得が遅れる場合が多い。私たちはみな，他者の唇に表れた言葉と聞こえてくる言葉を一体化しないではいられない。異なる感覚を通じて受け取った情報を脳はどのように組織化しているのか——会話の多感覚知覚に関する近年の研究によって，その理解に革命が起こった。

脳をさまざまな工具を収めたキャンピングナイフにたとえる，以前の（神経科学者や心理学者の）考え方は，いまではほとんど放棄された。脳のなかに異種の感覚をそれぞれ専門に扱う領域が別々にあるのではなく，脳は異種感覚の間のクロストークを最大限に利用するように進化してきたのだと現在では考えられている。脳の感覚領域は実際に絡み合っているという見方だ。私たちの感覚は常に互いを盗み聞きし，ある感覚が別の感覚にちょっかいを出している。例えば，脳の視覚野は主に視覚に関係してはいるものの，それ以外の感覚情報を解釈する完璧な能力も備えている。目の見える人が目隠しをつけると，90 分後には視覚野の働きによって接触刺激に非常に敏感になる。同様に，盲人では視覚野の神経配線が聴覚向けに自然に組み替わることが脳画像によって示されている。

ポテトチップスを食べるとき，パリパリする音がおいしさの決め手の 1 つだが，この音を少し変えて聞かせると，味覚まで変わってくる。また，動かずに立っているとき，どこの何を見ているかによって，その人の全身の姿勢が決まってくる。要は，どの感覚も単独で働いているのではないことが過去 15 年の研究で実証されたのだ。この“多感覚革命”は，人工内耳をはじめとする知覚障害者向けの

この記事の読み方

視覚や聴覚といった個々の感覚からの情報は，独立しているわけではなく，互いに補強し合う関係にある。記事ではこのテーマがあつかわれている。

複数の感覚の情報が合わさることを sensory integration/synthesis（感覚統合）という。これによって生じる知覚が multisensory perception（多感覚知覚）。multimodal perception（マルチモーダル知覚）ともいう。文中の multisensory revolution（多感覚革命）という表現はいささか大げさな気もするが，かつては個々の感覚が互いに独立したものとみなされていたことを考えれば，大きな変化には違いない。

多感覚知覚を示す例として示されているのは，lipreading（読唇術）と McGurk effect（マガーク効果）。小見出しの“Silent Syllables”は，無音（すなわち口パク）の音節のこと。邦訳は「マガーク効果」に変えてある。記事の後半では，相手がだれかという認識に多重の感覚情報が用いられていることが解説されている。

原題は“A Confederacy of Senses”（感覚たちの共謀）。共謀というと，なにかしら悪事を企むようなイメージ。邦題は「助け合う感覚」にしてある。

機器を改良する新たな方法にもつながるだろう。

マガーク効果

最も早くから知られていた多感覚知覚の明確な例は 1976 年にマガーク（Harry McGurk）とマクドナルド（John MacDonald）が報告したもので，「マガーク効果」と呼ばれている。「ガ」という音節を繰り返し発音している人の無音ビデオを見ながら，同じ人が「バ」と発音している録音テープを聞くと，「ダ」と言っているように聞こえる。目で見た「ガ」が，「バ」という実際に耳に入った音節の知覚を変化させているわけで，これは聞いたものと見たものを脳が統合しているからだ。このマガーク効果はあらゆる言語で生じ，長年これを研究して錯覚であることを理解している人でも生じる。25 年間研究している私自身が請け合う。

耳にした言葉は触覚の影響も受ける。1991 年，当時ダートマス大学にいたファウラー（Carol Fowler）らは，視覚と聴覚の二重障害者が用いる「タドマ法」という方法を未経験の被験者に試してもらった。タドマ法は相手の唇や頬，首に指で触れて，相手が話している内容を解釈するもので，人工内耳の登場前は多くの視覚聴覚二重障害者がこれに頼っていた（ヘレン・ケラーもその 1 人）。実験の結果，被験者が指で感じた音節によって，近くのスピーカーから聞こえてくる音節の聞こえ方が変わった。

1997 年には，当時英オックスフォード大学にいたカルバート（Gemma Calvert）が読唇術の実行中に最も活性化する脳領域を明らかにした。正式な読唇術を学んだ経験のない人たちに，1 から 9 までの数字を順にゆっくりと発音している顔を見せ，その唇を読んでもらったところ，音を処理する聴覚野のほか，発話を聞き取っている際に活性化することが知られている複数の関連領域も活性化した。単一の感覚の処理に特化していると考えられていた脳領域に異種感覚が影響することを示したのは，これが最初の例だったといえる。より最近の研究も感覚統合を裏づけている。例えば，以前はごく基本的な音の処理に関わっているだけだとみられていた聴性脳幹が，話者の顔を見た際にも反応することがわかっている。また脳画像研究によって，マガーク効果が生じている間，つまり「バ」という音を聞いているのに「ダ」と聞こえているときには，脳は「ダ」という音が耳に入っているかのように活動することが示された。

これらの発見は，耳と目，さらには皮膚を通じて漏れ伝わってきたそれぞれのスピーチ（発話）に，脳が同じウエートを置いていることをうかがわせる。もちろん，これら個別の感覚モダリティーが同じ量の情報をもたらしているというのではない。視覚や触覚よりも聴覚のほうが音声の詳細をとらえているのは明らかだ。脳はいろいろな感覚モダリティーを通じて得た異なるタイプのスピーチ情報をしっかり受け止めて組み合わせるために，協調的に働いているのだ。

顔にみんな書いてある

同じタイプの情報を処理するために異種感覚が助け合う場合もある。例えば話しぶりは，そのスピーチを耳で聞いた場合も目で唇を読んだ場合も，話者が誰なのかに関する情報をもたらす。私は共同研究者とともに，話している人をビデオに撮影し，その画像を加工して，顔から目鼻や口など目に見える特徴をすべて取り除いた。顔を複数の輝点に変換し，本来なら頬や唇が見えるはずのところにそれらに対応する輝点を表示して，蛍があちこち飛び回っているようなパターンに変えたのだ。このビデオを見た被験者たちは，輝点集団の動きだけで唇を読むことができ，その人物が自分の友人であることも認識できた。

スピーチに由来する単純な音声を聞いただけでも，話者が誰であるかについて重要な情報が得られる。コロンビア大学のレメズ（Robert Remez）らはスピーチを録音し，その音声を正弦波に還元した。それは『スター・ウォーズ』に出てくる R2-D2 が出すような機械的で奇妙な音声のように聞こえる。音の高低や音色など声の特徴を表す典型的な要素を欠いているのに，これらの正弦波は話しぶりに関する情報をそのまま保持していて，聞いた人はそれが友人の声であると認識できた。さらに驚いたことに，被験者たちはこれらの正弦波と，その同じ人についての先ほどの輝点パターンのビデオを正しく対応づけることもできた。

このように，耳で聞いたスピーチを簡略化したバージョンも，目で“見た”スピーチを簡略化したバージョンも，いずれも話しぶりに関する同様の情報を保持している。これは，これらの異なる知覚モードが脳のなかで絡み合っていることをうかがわせる。そして脳画像研究もこの関連を裏づけている。よく知っている人の声を聞いたときには，顔の認識に関連する「紡錘状回」という脳領域の神経活動が誘発されるのだ。

これらの発見に触発されて，少し奇抜な予測が生まれた。これらの知覚形態が混ざり合っているのなら，読唇術を習得すれば発話を聞き取る能力も高まるはずだ。私たちは読唇術の心得のない人たちに，話者を撮影した無音ビデオを1時間見せ，唇を読んでもらった。その後，ランダムノイズの背景に重ねた一連の文を聞かせた。被験者にはそれと知らせず，被験者の半数には先ほどのビデオでその唇を読んだばかりの人物が発話した文を聞かせ，他の半分にはビデオとは別の話者によるものを聞かせた。この結果，唇を読んだのと同じ人の発話した文を聞いたグループのほうが，背景ノイズからそれをうまく聞き取ることができた。

Lawrence D. Rosenblum
米カリフォルニア大学リバーサイド校で心理学の教授を務めている。著書に “See What I'm Saying: The Extraordinary Powers of Our Five Senses”〔W.W.Norton，2010（邦訳は『最新脳科学でわかった五感の驚異』講談社）〕がある。

Smells Like Old Times

匂いと記憶の深い関係

M. コニコヴァ
(サイエンスライター)

Smells Like Old Times

Our sense of smell sways our memory and thought

By Maria Konnikova

匂いの感覚は記憶と思考を左右している

KEY CONCEPTS

鼻が生み出す記憶

■匂いに結びついた記憶は他の記憶よりも強い場合がある。

■想起される視覚的記憶のほとんどは10代や20代前半の出来事なのに対し，匂い関連の記憶の多くは6～10歳の出来事に由来している。

■嗅覚の衰えは認知力低下の兆しであると考えられ，記憶の喪失を加速している可能性もある。

日経サイエンス2013年9月号，SCIENTIFIC AMERICAN MIND March/April 2012

Six years ago, on an early morning in September, Molly Birnbaum was out for her regular jog when she was hit by a car. Her pelvis was shattered, her skull fractured, her knee torn. Yet for her, the most serious damage was far less visible: she lost her sense of smell. Birnbaum, now 29, was an aspiring chef, and the loss meant the end of her career. It also meant something else, something that was potentially even more life-changing. "I felt like I lost a dimension of my memory," she says. "It made me worried about the future. If I couldn't smell ever again, was I losing this important layer?"

Vocabulary

out 外出して
pelvis 骨盤
shattered 砕けた
fractured 骨折した
torn 断裂した
sense of smell 嗅覚
torn 裂けた
aspiring chef シェフを目指している人
a dimension of ～の一面
memory 記憶
layer 記憶の層, 記憶の蓄積

Memory comes in many forms. Every day we constantly receive and process sights, sounds, touches and smells from our surroundings, some of which will become our memories. The nature of those recollections, however, is inconstant. One memory can seem immediate and colorful, as if the event had just occurred, whereas another must be coaxed out of our brain little by little. Although a moment that excites our emotions is more likely to be recorded than a routine experience, the sensory qualities of the event we have buried in our brain also plays a part in how vividly and accurately we remember something.

come in many forms （～には）さまざまな形がある
sights 見えるもの
touches 触れるもの
surrounding 周囲（の状況）
recollection 記憶, 思い出
inconstant 一定ではない
immediate 即時の, 直接的な
whereas ～であるのに対し, 一方
coax 引き出す, 搾り出す
bury 埋める
play a part 一役買う
accurately 正確に

Although sight dominates our daily life, it has long been thought that smell might have a privileged relation with memory. Until relatively recently, however, the precise nature of that connection remained largely unexplored. Now scientists are revealing that recollections tied to smell can be stronger than memory of other types. Olfaction can transport our thoughts back to some of our earliest experiences and tint these remembrances with feeling. On the flip side, its absence could be a sign—and potentially a cause—of cognitive decline. Scientists are at a very early stage of developing therapies to train people to smell better, which could one day stave off the deterioration of mental faculties.

sight 視覚
dominate 優位を占める
privileged 特権的な, 特別な
unexplored 探られていない
reveal 明らかにする
olfaction 嗅覚
tint 色づけする
remembrance 思い出, 回想
on the flip side その一方で, 逆に, 裏返していうと
cognitive decline 認知機能の低下
stave off 食い止める
deterioration of mental faculties 心的能力の低下

Transported by Scent

Aristotle explored the apparent ties between odor and memory in his treatise from the fourth century B.C., On Sense and the Sensible. Since then, people have speculated that the memories elicited by smell are more intimate and immediate than other recollections. When we experience certain smells, we often find ourselves whisked back in time to a specific event or scene. For example, the smell of salsa reminded Birnbaum of watching James Bond movies on television with her dad while dipping chips in the spicy sauce. When she lost her sense of smell, she could still remember eating salsa with her father, but she could no longer quickly summon that long-ago scenario. xx

Psychology studies support the idea that memories associated with odors are unusually evocative.In a 2006 experiment psychologists Johan Willander and Maria Larsson of Stockholm University gave older adults one of three types of cues—visual, auditory or olfactory—and asked them to describe an autobiographical event that came to mind as a result. The participants also rated the event based on its emotionality, vividness and importance.

Although the volunteers came up with the same number of memories for each type of cue, odors elicited earlier memories, including far more from the first 10 years of life, than did sight or sound cues. Recollections emerging from scents were also associated with a stronger feeling of being brought back in time. The results suggest that memories tied to smell are both older and associated with a more time travel–like experience than are other types.

The use of odors to trigger memories has led researchers to reconsider the long-held notion that people recall more incidents from their teens and 20s than from any other time in their life. In 2000 psychologist Simon Chu, now at the University of Central Lancashire in England, and his colleagues discovered that although visual memories did

Vocabulary

scent 匂い
Aristotle アリストテレス
odor 匂い
treatise 論文
the sensible 感知できるもの
speculate 推測する
elicit 引き出す, 呼び起こす
intimate 詳細な
whisked back in time 時間を遡って
summon 呼び出す

associated with ～と関連した, ～と結びついた
evocative 想起されやすい
cue キュー（手がかりとなる刺激）
▶この記事の読み方
auditory 聴覚的な
olfactory 嗅覚的な
autobiographical 自伝的な, 自分自身に関する
emotionality 感情的興奮度
vividness 鮮明さ

come up with 思い浮かぶ
emerge from ～から生じる, ～から思い浮かぶ
brought back in time 昔に呼び戻される

trigger ～の引き金となる, ～のきっかけとなる
reconsider 見直す
long-held notion 長年の定説
incident 出来事
colleague 共同研究者

peak between the ages of 11 and 25, odor-cued recollections crested between the ages of six and 10.

Rachel Herz, a cognitive neuroscientist at Brown University, sees olfaction as a potential key to a trove of past experiences that would otherwise remain locked. A whiff of a smell not encountered since childhood may bring us back to an event that we had all but forgotten existed, she theorizes.

Smell might have this power because odors themselves are relatively rare, compared with, say, visual stimuli. Every day our eyes are constantly bombarded with images, many of which are quite similar, creating confusing interference in the brain. In contrast, our nose detects distinct odors only infrequently, a fact that Richard L. Doty, director of the Smell and Taste Center at the University of Pennsylvania, surmises is key to the evocative power of scent. Because smells are encountered rarely, individual odors are often tied to a unique experience, enabling a strong and stable connection.

Smell has a privileged relation with memory on an anatomical level as well. It is the only sense that connects with the memory system without stopping over in the thalamus, a sensory relay station. Signals travel from the nose to the olfactory bulb and then directly to the hippocampus, an essential hub of memory formation, and the amygdala, which processes emotion. "Memory and odors are just sitting side by side," says research psychiatrist Donald Wilson of New York University Langone Medical Center.

The connection does not end there. In a parallel track, the olfactory bulb passes information to the olfactory cortex, which sits at the surface of the brain just above the ears. Part of this region is involved in complex learning and memory tasks. The olfactory cortex, together with an adjacent decision-making area, the orbitofrontal cortex,

Vocabulary

crest ピークとなる

cognitive neuroscientist 認知神経科学者
trove 宝庫
otherwise それがなければ
a whiff of a smell かすかな匂い
theorize 理論を立てる

say 例えば
bombarded with ～を浴びる
confusing interference 混同, 混乱を招く干渉
in contrast 対照的に
infrequently まれに
surmise 推察する

anatomical 解剖学的な
stop over in ～を経由する
thalamus 視床
sensory relay station 感覚信号の中継基地
olfactory bulb 嗅球
hippocampus 海馬
▶この記事の読み方
essential hub of memory formation 記憶形成の中枢
amygdala 扁桃体
▶この記事の読み方
emotion 情動
sit side by side 隣り合う

in a parallel track それと並行して
olfactory cortex 嗅覚皮質
▶この記事の読み方
involved in ～に関与している
adjacent 隣接している
orbitofrontal cortex 眼窩前頭皮質
back-and-forth communication

processes the information contained in a smell and sends the data back to the hippocampus. This back-and-forth communication ties scents with remembrances.

Vocabulary

情報のやりとり

Sniffs of Young Noses

To understand why odors seem to strongly evoke very early life experiences, scientists began to search for other differences in how the senses interact with memory. In 2009 neuroscientist Noam Sobel of the Weizmann Institute of Science in Rehovot, Israel, and his colleagues taught subjects to pair pictures of objects with a smell or a sound, or both. Subjects then viewed pictures of the objects while in an MRI scanner and were asked to recall either the smell or sound associated with each image. In a second round, the researchers paired every object with an opposing odor or sound or odor-sound pair: if the first stimulus had been pleasant, this time, it was unpleasant—and vice versa. Another brain scan and test of these memories followed.

sniff 嗅ぐこと，嗅ぎ分け
evoke 呼び起こす
interact with ～と相互作用する
subject 被験者
opposing 逆の，反対の
and vice versa 逆もまたしかり

One week later the researchers presented the pictures a third time and asked participants to name the odor or sound that popped into their mind. Overall, people recalled the memories from the first round slightly more than those in the second set. The brain scans, however, produced a more nuanced picture. When a person thought of the first odor, the hippocampus became much more active than when he or she remembered the second smell, suggesting that the brain issues a special tag for first odor associations. In contrast, the hippocampus activity was the same for first and second sounds.

participant 被験者，実験参加者
pop into someone's mind 思い浮かぶ
nuanced 微妙な
issue a tag タグをつける
association 関連づけ，連想

In addition, on the first memory test, the more the hippocampus responded during odor retrieval, the more likely a person was to later remember that first odor as opposed to the second. No such relation existed for sounds. Given the brain's unique response to first odor memories, the smells of childhood may make early remembrances particularly durable.

odor retrieval 匂いの想起
durable 長持ちする，あせない

Although its effect on our earliest recollections may be most pronounced, smell might also facilitate learning more broadly. In a study published in 2007 neuroendocrinologist Jan Born and his colleagues at the University of Lübeck in Germany asked people to inhale the smell of a rose while studying the locations of 15 pairs of cards on a computer screen. When the participants went to sleep that night in the lab, some of them were exposed to the rose odor, whereas others' sleep was unscented. In the morning, all the participants were tested on their memory for the card locations. Those who had been exposed to the flower fragrance remembered 97 percent of them, compared with just 86 percent for those who had received an odorless stimulus, suggesting that odors can boost learning as memories are consolidated during sleep.

Vocabulary

pronounced 顕著な
facilitate 促進する, 助ける
neuroendocrinologist 神経内分泌学者
inhale 吸い込む
location 配置
lab 実験室
expose さらす
unscented 匂いのない
boost 強化する, 促進する
consolidate 強固にする

6年前の9月のある朝，モリー・バーンバウム（Molly Birnbaum）は日課のジョギング中に車にはねられた。頭と腰の骨が砕け，膝は断裂した。しかし彼女にとって最も深刻なダメージは，見た目にはずっとわかりにくいものだった。匂いの感覚が失われたのだ。現在29歳になったバーンバウムは事故当時，シェフを目指して腕を磨いていたところで，嗅覚喪失は料理人としてのキャリアの終わりを意味した。そして，ひょっとすると生活をもっと大きく変えてしまう別の事柄をも意味していた。「多くの記憶を失ったように感じた」と彼女はいう。「この先どうなるのかと不安になった。もし嗅覚が戻らなかったら，大切な記憶の蓄積を失うことになるのでは……」。

記憶はさまざまな形で生じる。私たちは毎日，視覚や聴覚，触覚，嗅覚を通じて周囲の状況を常にとらえて処理しており，その一部が記憶となる。だが，記憶の性質は同じではない。ある記憶はたったいま起こった出来事のように精彩に富んでいるが，別の記憶は頭の奥から少しずつ搾り出さねばならない。日常的な経験よりも感情を強く揺さぶる出来事のほうが記憶に残りやすいとはいえ，記憶をどれだけ生き生きと正確に想起できるかは，脳に埋められた出来事の感覚の質にも左右される。

日常生活では視覚の役割が大きいものの，匂いは記憶と特別な関係があるらしいと昔から考えられてきた。ただ，この関係が正確に調べられるようになったのは比較的最近になってからだ。現在では，匂いに結びついた記憶は他の記憶よりも強いことが明らかになりつつある。嗅覚は人の思考を昔の体験へと導き，そうした回想を感情で色づけする。裏返していうと，その欠如は認知力低下の兆しであり，ひょっとすると原因となっている可能性もある。嗅覚を高める訓練によって，いずれは認知機能の衰えを食い止められるかもしれない──そうした治療法の開発が，非常に初期の段階ではあるが，すでに始まっている。

匂いでタイムトラベル

アリストテレスは匂いと記憶の間に見られるこのつながりを，紀元前4世紀の著作『感覚と感覚されるものについて』で論じている。以来，匂いによって呼び起こされた記憶はその他の記憶よりも詳細で鮮明であると考えられてきた。ある種の匂いを嗅いだときに，昔の特定の出来事や光景が急によみがえることがしばしばある。バーンバウムの場合はサルサソースの匂いがそれで，これを嗅ぐと，かつて父親とフライドポテトをサルサソースにつけて食べながらテレビで007の映画を観たことを思い出した。しかし嗅覚を失ってからは，父親と一緒にサルサソースでポテトを食べたこと自体は思い出せるものの，以前のようにその記憶を瞬時に呼び出すことはできなくなった。

匂いと結びついた記憶が特に想起されやすいことは心理学研究で裏づけられている。ストックホルム大学の心理学者ウィランダー（Johan Willander）とラーソン（Maria Larsson）は2006年の実験で，視覚・聴覚・嗅覚の3タイプのうちどれか1つのキュー（手がかりとなる刺激）を熟年者に与え，どんな自伝的記憶（自分自身に関する事柄の記憶）が思い浮かんだかを尋ねた。被験者はまた，想起したその出来事を感情的興奮度と鮮明さ，重要性に基づいて格付けした。

どのタイプのキューも同数の記憶を呼び起こしたが，匂いは視覚や聴覚のキューよりも昔の記憶を呼び起こし，なかには10歳以前の出来事も多く含まれていた。また，昔に呼び戻されるような感覚を強く伴っていた。匂いに結びついた記憶は他の記憶よりも古く，タイムトラベルに似た経験をもたらすことを示している。

匂いを記憶想起のきっかけに使ったこれらの実験は，人は人生のなかで10代と20代の出来事を最もよく思い出すという長年の定説に見直しを迫った。現在は英セントラル・ランカシャー大学にいる心理学者チュー（Simon Chu）らは2000年，視覚的な記憶は確かに11～25歳の体験がピークだが，匂いが手がかりとなって想起される記憶は6～10歳の出来事がピークとなることを見いだした。

ブラウン大学の認知神経科学者ハーツ（Rachel Herz）は嗅覚を，過去の体験を収めて封印してある箱を開ける鍵なのだとみている。子どものころに体験して以来ずっと嗅いだことのなかった匂いをちょっと嗅いだだけで，忘れ去ったも同然だった出来事がまざまざとよみがえるのだという。

匂いにこの力があるのは，匂い自体が視覚刺激などに比べてまれであるためかもしれない。私たちの目は毎日絶え間なく映像にさらされており，その多くは似たり寄ったりで，脳のなかで混同を引き起こす。鼻はこれと対照的に，はっきりした匂いをたまに検出するだけだ。これが匂いの記憶想起力の鍵を握っているのだとペンシルベニア大学嗅覚味覚センター所長のドティ（Richard L. Doty）はみている。匂いに遭遇するのはまれなので，それぞれの匂いが特定の体験に結びつくことが多く，強くて安定したつながりが生まれる。

匂いは解剖学的な面でも記憶と特別な関係がある。感覚信号の中継基地である視床を経由せずに記憶系に直接結びついている感覚は嗅覚だけだ。嗅覚信号は鼻から脳の「嗅球」に送られ，そこから記憶形成の中枢である海馬と，情動を処理している扁桃体に送られる。「記憶と匂いは脳のなかで隣り合っている」とニューヨーク大学ランゴーン医療センターの精神科医ウィルソン（Donald

この記事の読み方

冒頭では，シェフを目指していた女性が事故に遭い嗅覚を失ったケースが紹介されている。anosmia（無嗅覚症／アノスミア）と呼ばれる嗅覚障害である。彼女は匂いがわからなくなっただけでなく，記憶の想起も困難になってしまった。このことは匂いと記憶の緊密な結びつきを示している。

ここでいう記憶は，思い出などの episodic memory（エピソード記憶）のこと。autobiographical memory（自伝的記憶）とも呼ばれる。匂いはそれらの記憶を引き出す cues（手がかり）になる。記事では，記憶形成の中枢の hippocampus（海馬），情動の中枢である amygdala（扁桃体），そして嗅覚の中枢である olfactory cortex（嗅覚皮質）がどのように連絡しあっているかが解説され，匂いが記憶を引き出すメカニズムが推測されている。

このように嗅覚障害は嗅覚だけの問題ではない。記事の後半では，認知症における嗅覚と記憶の障害の関係にも言及している。

記事の原題は “Smells Like Old Times”（昔のような匂いがする）。It smells の It が省略されている。

Wilson）はいう。

それだけではない。嗅球は匂いの情報を嗅覚皮質に送る。嗅覚皮質は両耳のすぐ上にある脳領域で，その一部は学習と記憶の複雑な処理に関与している。嗅覚皮質は意思決定に関わる眼窩前頭皮質という隣接領域とともに匂いの情報を処理し，その結果を海馬に送っている。こうした情報のやり取りによって，匂いと記憶が結びつく。

脳画像が示すつながり

匂いが遠い子どものころの体験を強く呼び起こすのはなぜなのか。その理由を探るため，科学者たちはさまざまな感覚が記憶にどう影響するかを調べ始めた。イスラエルのレホボトにあるワイツマン科学研究所の神経科学者ソーベル（Noam Sobel）は 2009 年の実験で，物体を撮影した写真に匂いまたは音，あるいはその両方を結びつけて被験者に覚えさせた。その後，磁気共鳴画像装置（MRI）で脳を撮影しながら被験者にそれらの写真を見せ，それぞれの写真に関連づけた匂いや音を思い出してもらった。そして次の回では，それぞれの写真に前回とは逆の匂いと音を結びつけた。前回の刺激が心地よい匂いだった場合，今回は不快な匂いにするといった具合だ。そのうえで同様の脳スキャンとテストを行った。

1 週間後に 3 回目のテストを行い，写真を見てどの匂いや音が思い浮かんだかを尋ねた。2 回目よりも 1 回目のテストで関連づけた匂いや音を思い出す例が総じてわずかに多かった。そして，さらに微妙なことが脳画像から明らかになった。被験者が 1 回目の匂いを想起しているときは，2 回目の匂いを思い出している場合よりも海馬の活動がはるかに活発になったのだ。これは脳が 1 回目の匂いの関連づけに特別な認識タグをつけていることをうかがわせる。これと対照的に，音については 1 回目の音と 2 回目の音の想起で海馬の活動は同じだった。

さらに，1 回目のテストで匂いを想起している際に海馬が活発に反応していた場合ほど，その人は 3 回目のテストにおいて 2 回目ではなく 1 回目の匂いを思い出す傾向が強かった。こうした関連は音については見られなかった。

最初の匂い記憶に対する脳のこの特異な反応から，子どものころに嗅いだ匂いが，その記憶をとりわけ確固たるものにしているのだと考えられる。

昔の記憶を呼び起こすこの効果は最も顕著なものだが，匂いはもっと広い意味でも学習を助けている可能性がある。独リューベック大学の神経内分泌学者ボルン（Jan Born）らは2007年に発表した研究で，被験者がコンピューター画面に表示されたトランプ15組の配置を見て覚えている間に，バラの香りを嗅いでもらった。その夜，実験室で被験者が眠っている間に，一部の被験者を同じバラの匂いにさらした。翌朝，全員がカードの配置についての記憶テストを受けた。睡眠中に匂い刺激を受けなかった人たちはカード配置の86%を覚えていただけだったのに対し，バラの香りにさらされていた人は97%を記憶していた。睡眠中に起こる記憶の固定を匂いが促進したのだと考えられる。

Maria Konnikova
米ニューヨーク在住のライター。著書に“Mastermind: How to Think Like Sherlock Holmes”〔Penguin, 2013（邦訳は『シャーロック・ホームズの思考術』ハヤカワ文庫NF）〕がある。

Perchance to Prune

眠りが刈り込む余計な記憶

G. トノーニ／C. チレッリ
（ともに米ウィスコンシン大学）

Perchance to Prune

During sleep, the brain weakens the connections among nerve cells, apparently conserving energy and, paradoxically, aiding memory

By Giulio Tononi and Chiara Cirelli

睡眠中，脳はニューロン間の結びつきを実は弱める
そうやってエネルギーを節約し，意外にも記憶を補強しているようだ

KEY CONCEPTS

シナプスを弱めることで記憶を強化する

■すべての動物は睡眠をとる。睡眠は必要不可欠な何らかの役割を果たしているに違いない。

■睡眠がニューロン間の結びつきを弱めていることを示す証拠がある。覚醒時にはそうした神経接続の強化が学習や記憶を助けることからすると，これは意外な作用だ。

■しかし，睡眠はシナプスを弱めることによって，脳細胞が日常経験によって過飽和になったり，エネルギーを消費しすぎたりするのを防いでいる可能性がある。

日経サイエンス 2013 年 11 月号，SCIENTIFIC AMERICAN August 2013

Every night, while we lie asleep, blind, dumb and almost paralyzed, our brains are hard at work. Neurons in the sleeping brain fire nearly as often as they do in a waking state, and they consume almost as much energy. What is the point of this unceasing activity at a time when we are supposedly resting? Why does the conscious mind disconnect so completely from the external environment while the brain keeps nattering on?

The brain's activity during rest likely serves some essential function. The evidence for this importance starts with sleep's ubiquity. All animals apparently sleep even though being unconscious and unresponsive greatly raises the risk of becoming another creature's lunch. Birds do it, bees do it, iguanas and cockroaches do it, even fruit flies do it, as we and others demonstrated more than a decade ago.

Furthermore, evolution has devised a few extraordinary adaptations to accommodate sleep: dolphins and some other marine mammals that must surface often to breathe, for example, sleep by alternately switching off one hemisphere of their brain while the other remains in a waking state.

Like many scientists and nonscientists, the two of us have long wondered what benefit sleep provides that makes it so crucial to living creatures. More than 20 years ago, when we worked together at the Sant'Anna School of Advanced Studies in Pisa, Italy, we began to suspect that the brain's activity during slumber may somehow restore to a baseline state the billions of neural connections that get modified every day by the events of waking life. Sleep, in this telling, would preserve the ability of the brain's circuitry to form new memories continually over the course of an individual's lifetime without becoming oversaturated or obliterating older memories.

Vocabulary

［タイトル］ **perchance** おそらく
prune 刈り込む
▶この記事の読み方

dumb 口をきかない
paralyzed 麻痺状態の
neuron ニューロン, 神経細胞
fire 発火する
waking state 覚醒状態
point 意味
unceasing 絶え間ない
conscious mind 意識
disconnect 遮断される
natter on しゃべり続ける, 活動し続ける

essential 重要な
ubiquity 普遍性
unconscious 無意識の
unresponsive 無反応の
lunch 餌食
fruit fly ショウジョウバエ

evolution 進化
devise 考え出す
extraordinary 並外れた
adaptation 適応
accommodate ～に対応する
marine mammal 海洋哺乳類
surface 浮上する
alternately 交互に
switch off 休ませる
hemisphere 半球

benefit メリット
suspect ～ではないかと考える
slumber 眠り
restore 戻す
baseline state 基本状態
neural connection 神経接続
modified 変更された
telling 仮説
preserve 維持する
circuitry 神経回路
over the course of ～にわたって
oversaturated 過飽和である
obliterate 消去する

We also have an idea of why awareness of the external environment must be shut off during sleep. It seems to us that conscious experience of the here and now has to be interrupted for the brain to gain the chance to integrate new and old memories; sleep provides that respite.

Our hypothesis is somewhat controversial among our fellow neuroscientists who study sleep's role in learning and memory because we suggest that the return to baseline results from a weakening of the links among the neurons that fire during sleep. Conventional wisdom holds, instead, that brain activity during sleep strengthens the neural connections involved in storing newly formed memories. Yet years of research with organisms ranging from flies to people lend support to our notions.

School of Nod

Scientists first proposed the idea that sleep is important to memory nearly a century ago, and plenty of experiments since then have shown that after a night of sleep, and sometimes just a nap, newly formed memories "stick" better than they would if one had spent the same amount of time awake. This pattern holds for declarative memories, such as lists of words and associations between pictures and places, as well as for procedural memories, which underlie perceptual and motor skills, such as playing a musical instrument.

The evidence that sleep benefits memory led scientists to look for signs that the brain rehashes newly learned material at night. They found them: studies performed over the past 20 years, first in rodents and then in humans, show that patterns of neural activity during sleep sometimes do resemble those recorded while subjects are awake. For example, when a rat learns to navigate a maze, certain neurons in a part of the brain called the hippocampus fire in specific sequences. During subsequent sleep, rats "replay" these sequences more often than predicted by chance.

Vocabulary

awareness 認識，意識
shut off 遮断する
interrupt 中断させる
integrate 統合する
respite 小休止

hypothesis 仮説
controversial 物議をかもす
neuroscientist 神経科学者
link 結びつき
conventional wisdom 従来の知見
hold ～と考える
instead そうではなく，逆に
lend support 支持する

nap 昼寝
stick 心にとどまる，長持ちする
holds for ～に当てはまる
declarative memory 陳述記憶
▶この記事の読み方
association 対応づけ
procedural memory 手続き記憶
underlie ～の基本にある
perceptual 知覚の
motor 運動の

benefit 役立つ，プラスに働く
rehash 反芻する
rodent 齧歯動物（ネズミなど）
resemble ～に似ている
subject 実験動物，被験者
rat ラット
navigate 通り抜ける
maze 迷路
hippocampus 海馬
sequence 順序
subsequent その後の
chance 偶然

Because of such findings, many researchers came to assume that sleep "replay" consolidates memories by further reinforcing synapses—the contact points between neurons—that have been strengthened when an individual is awake. The idea is that, as linked neurons fire repeatedly, the synapses connecting them more readily convey signals from one neuron to another, helping neuronal circuits to encode memories in the brain. This process of selective strengthening is known as synaptic potentiation, and it is the favored mechanism by which the brain is thought to accomplish learning and remembering.

Vocabulary

consolidate 強固にする
reinforce 強化する
synapse シナプス
readily 容易に
neuronal circuit 神経回路
encode 符号化する, コード化する
selective strengthening 選択的強化
synaptic potentiation シナプス増強
favored 支持された

Yet while replay and potentiation are known to occur during waking activities, scientists have so far found no direct evidence that the synapses in replayed circuits get strengthened during sleep. This lack of evidence hardly surprises us. It is consistent with our suspicion that while the sleeper lies unaware, all that brain activity—the "replay" as well as other, seemingly random firings—might actually be weakening neural connections, not strengthening them.

so far これまで
hardly ほとんど～ない
consistent with ～と整合する
suspicion 疑念
seemingly 一見

The Price of Plasticity

There are many good reasons to propose that synapses must become weakened as well as strengthened for the brain to function properly. For one thing, strong synapses consume more energy than weak ones, and the brain does not have infinite stores of energy. In humans the brain accounts for almost 20 percent of the body's energy budget—more than any other organ by weight—and at least two thirds of that portion goes to supporting synaptic activity. Building and bolstering synapses is also a major source of cellular stress, requiring cells to synthesize and deliver components ranging from mitochondria (the cell's power plants), to synaptic vesicles (which ferry signaling molecules), to various proteins and lipids that are needed for communication across synapses.

price 代価
plasticity 可塑性
for one thing 1つには
infinite 無限の
account for 占める
organ 器官
by weight 重量比で見て
synaptic activity シナプス活動
build 形成する
bolster 増強する
cellular stress 細胞ストレス, ニューロンの負担
deliver 受け渡す
mitochondria ミトコンドリア
synaptic vesicle シナプス小胞
ferry 運ぶ
signaling molecule シグナル分子
lipid 脂質

It seems clear to us that this strain on resources is unsustainable. The brain cannot go on strengthening and maintaining revved-up synapses both day and night for the whole of an individual's lifetime. We do not doubt that learning occurs mainly through synaptic potentiation. We simply doubt that strengthening continues to happen during sleep.

In contrast, synaptic weakening during sleep would restore brain circuitry to a baseline level of strength, thereby avoiding excessive energy consumption and cellular stress. We refer to this baseline-restoring function of sleep as preserving synaptic homeostasis, and we call our overall hypothesis about the role of sleep the synaptic homeostasis hypothesis, or SHY. In principle, SHY explains the essential, universal purpose of sleep for all organisms that do it: sleep restores the brain to a state where it can learn and adapt when we are awake. The risk we take by becoming disconnected from the environment for hours at a time is the price we pay for this neural recalibration. Most generally, sleep is the price we pay for the brain's plasticity—its ability to modify its wiring in response to experience.

But how does SHY explain sleep's salutary effects on learning and memory? How can weakened synapses improve the overall retention of skills and facts? Consider that, over the course of a typical day, almost everything you experience leaves a neural trace in the brain and that the significant events, like meeting a new person or learning a piece of music on the guitar, make up just a trifling portion of that neural encoding. To improve memory, the sleeping brain must somehow distinguish the "noise" of irrelevant information from the "signal" of significant happenings.

We suggest that in sleep, the spontaneous firing of neurons in the brain activates many different circuits in many different combinations, encompassing both new memory traces and old networks of learned

Vocabulary

strain 負担
revved-up フル回転している

in contrast 対照的に
synaptic weakening シナプス弱化
refer to ~ as ～を…と呼ぶ
preserve 保存する
synaptic homeostasis hypothesis シナプス恒常性仮説
▶この記事の読み方
in principle 原則的に
universal 普遍的な
organism 生物
recalibration 再較正，再調整
wiring 配線
in response to ～に応じて

salutary 有益な
retention 記憶の保持
trace 痕跡
make up 構成する，占める
trifling わずかな
neural encoding 神経符号化
irrelevant 重要でない，取るに足らない

spontaneous 自発的な
encompass 包含する

associations. (You get a glimpse of this neural free-for-all in dreams.) The spontaneous activity lets the brain try out which new memories fit better with stored memories of proved significance and weakens those synapses that do not fit well in the grand scheme of memory. We and other investigators are exploring possible mechanisms by which brain activity could selectively weaken synapses that encode the "noise" while preserving those that correspond to the "signal."

While the brain tries out these imaginary scenarios and enacts weakening where appropriate, we had best be unaware of the surrounding environment and be incapable of acting in it; that is, we had best be asleep. Likewise, restoring synaptic homeostasis should not take place while we are awake because the events of the day would dominate the process, giving salience to them rather than to all the knowledge the brain has accumulated over a lifetime. The profound disconnection of sleep frees our brain from the tyranny of the present, creating an ideal circumstance for integrating and consolidating memories.

Vocabulary

get a glimpse of ～を垣間見る
free-for-all 混乱状態
grand scheme 壮大な計画
correspond to ～に対応する

try out 試す
imaginary 仮想的な
enact 実行する
where appropriate 適宜
had best ～するのが一番よい
dominate ～の主体となる
give salience 重視する，重点を置く
profound disconnection 完全な遮断状態
tyranny 専制支配

人は毎晩眠り，その間は何も見ず，口もきかず，ほとんど麻痺状態になっているが，脳はせっせと働いている。睡眠中の脳のニューロン（神経細胞）は，覚醒時とほぼ同じ頻度で発火し，ほぼ同程度のエネルギーを消費している。人が一見休息をしているように見える時，こうした絶え間ない活動をしている意味とは何だろう。また，脳が活動し続けているのに，意識はなぜ外界からこれほど完全に遮断されているのだろう。

睡眠中の脳の活動は，何らかの重要な役割を担っている可能性が高い。その第1の証拠は，睡眠があらゆる動物に普遍的であることだ。無意識・無反応の状態になると他者の餌食になるリスクは大きく高まるのに，すべての動物は睡眠をとるようだ。鳥もハチもイグアナもゴキブリも眠る。私たちは10年以上前，ショウジョウバエでさえ眠ることを確かめている。

しかも睡眠のためのいくつかの驚くべき適応が進化を通じてなされている。例えば，呼吸のため頻繁に浮上しなければならないイルカなどの海洋哺乳類は眠っている間，脳の半球を片方ずつ交互に休ませ，脳の片方が休む間はもう片方が覚醒状態を保つ。

睡眠が何の役に立ち，生物にとって欠かせないものになっているのかは，昔からの謎だった。私たちは，イタリア・ピサにある聖アンナ高等師範学校に共に勤務していた20年以上前，睡眠中の脳の活動が，覚醒時の出来事によって日々変更される何十億もの神経接続を，何らかの方法で基本状態に戻すのではないかと考え始めた。この仮説では，睡眠は，脳が記憶で過飽和になったり，古い記憶を消去したりすることなく，一生にわたって絶えず新たな記憶を形成できるようにしている。

睡眠中に外界の認識を遮断しなければならない理由についても，私たちは仮説を立てている。脳が新たな記憶を古い記憶と統合する際には，現在起きている事柄を意識する体験を一時的に中断する必要があるのだろう。そのための時間が睡眠によって与えられるのだ。

私たちの仮説は，睡眠の学習・記憶面の役割を研究している神経科学者の間で少しばかり物議をかもしている。というのも，ニューロンの状態復帰が起こるのは，発火するニューロンの間の結びつきが睡眠中に弱まることによると考えているからだ。従来の知見では逆に，睡眠中の脳の活動は，新たに形成された記憶の保存に関係した神経接続を強化するとされている。だが，ハエからヒトまでの生物についての長年の研究は，私たちの見方を裏づけている。

眠って学習

記憶にとって睡眠が重要であると科学者が最初に唱えたのは1世紀近く前のことで，以来，多くの実験が，一晩眠ったり，場合によってはちょっと昼寝をしたりした後，新しく覚えたことが，起きていた場合より長持ちすることを明らかにしてきた。これは，単語のリストや，写真と場所の対応づけといった「陳

この記事の読み方

眠っている時には，免疫系の活性化や各種ホルモンの分泌などさまざまなことが起こるが，記憶の整理（消去や強化）もその1つ。本記事では，そのカギがノンレム睡眠中のシナプスの弱化にあるという synaptic homeostasis hypothesis（シナプス恒常性仮説）が展開されている。

ニューロン（神経細胞）間の connection はここでは「接続」や「結びつき」と訳してある。「結合」という訳語も見かけることがあるが，化学結合のようなものではなく，シナプスによる回路を指しているので，「接続」という訳語のほうがより適切なように思われる。declarative memory は，「陳述記憶」や「宣言的記憶」と訳される（どちらを採用するかは好みの問題）が，「陳述」も「宣言」も裁判や政治の場面で使われることが多いため，心理学の専門外の人には，用語として少し奇異に感じられるかもしれない。

原題は “Perchance to Prune”。シェイクスピアの有名な戯曲『ハムレット』中のセリフ “To sleep, perchance to dream”（眠ると，たぶん夢を見る）をもじったもの。“To sleep” が省略されているが，“To sleep, perchance to prune”（眠ると，たぶん剪定が起きる）の意。

述記憶」にも，楽器の演奏といった，知覚・運動技能の基本にある「手続き記憶」にも当てはまる。

睡眠が記憶にプラスに働くことがわかったため，科学者たちは，新たに学習した内容を脳が夜間に反芻している証拠を探り，それを見つけた。当初はネズミ，その後はヒトを対象に過去 20 年間に実施された研究は，睡眠中の神経活動のパターンが，実験動物や被験者の覚醒時に記録されるパターンに似ている場合が確かにあることを明らかにしている。例えばラットが迷路の通り抜けを学習するときには，海馬という脳領域の特定のニューロンが決まった順序で発火する。その後の睡眠中，ラットの脳はこの順序を高い頻度で “リプレイ” する。

そうした研究結果から，多くの研究者は，睡眠中のリプレイが，覚醒中に強化されたシナプス（ニューロン間の接点）を強化することで記憶を強めると考えるようになった。つまり，連結されたニューロンが繰り返し発火するにつれ，ニューロンどうしをつないでいるシナプスが 1 つのニューロンから別のニューロンに信号をより容易に伝えるようになり，神経回路による脳内での記憶のコード化を助けるというわけだ。この選択的強化のプロセスは「シナプス増強」と呼ばれており，脳が学習と記憶を達成する想定メカニズムとして支持されている。

ただ，こうしたリプレイと増強作用が覚醒中に起こることはわかっているものの，リプレイされた神経回路のシナプスが睡眠中に強化されるという直接の証拠はまだ見つかっていない。私たちに言わせれば，それは当然だ。無意識状態で寝ている間，リプレイや一見ランダムなニューロンの発火という脳の活動が，神経接続を強めているのではなく，実は弱めているという私たちの考えと整合するのだ。

可塑性の代価

脳が適切に機能するためには，シナプスの強化だけでなく弱化も必要であると考える根拠は多数ある。1 つには，強いシナプスは弱いシナプスよりも多くのエネルギーを消費するが，脳はエネルギーを無尽蔵に蓄えているわけではない。ヒトの場合，脳は身体のエネルギーの 20%近く（重量比で見て他のどの器官よりも多い）を消費し，その少なくとも 2/3 はシナプス活動の維持に充てられている。また，シナプスの形成と増強は，ニューロンに大きな負担をかけており，細胞内の発電所に相当するミトコンドリアから，シグナル分子を運ぶシナプス小胞，シナプス間の連絡に必要なタンパク質や脂質に至るまでさまざまな要素の合成と受け渡しを細胞に要求する。

このような負担が持続不可能であることは明らかだ。フル回転しているシナプスの強化と維持を，脳が連日連夜，生涯にわたってやり続けることはできない。私たちは，学習が主としてシナプス増強によって行われることは疑っていないが，睡眠中にシナプスの強化がずっと続いているわけではないと考えている。

対照的に，睡眠中のシナプス弱化は脳の神経回路を元の強度に戻し，それによって過剰なエネルギー消費や細胞ストレスを回避する。私たちは，睡眠によるこの回復機能をシナプスの恒常性維持と呼び，そのような睡眠の役割に関する仮説を「シナプス恒常性仮説」と名づけている。この仮説によって原則的に，すべての眠る生物にとっての，睡眠の極めて重要で普遍的な目的が説明される。つまり睡眠によって，脳は覚醒時に学習や適応を行える状態に戻るのだ。睡眠中に何時間にもわたって環境から遮断されるリスクは，脳の可塑性，すなわち経験に応じて脳の配線を修正する能力のために支払う代価であるといえる。

シナプス恒常性仮説は，学習と記憶に及ぼす睡眠の有益な効果をどう説明するのだろうか。シナプス弱化は，技能や事実の記憶の保持をどのように改善するのだろうか。毎日経験するほぼすべての出来事は脳内に痕跡を残す一方で，新しい人との出会いやギターの練習といった重要な出来事は通常そうした記録のわずかな部分しか占めていない。記憶を強化するには，睡眠中の脳は，取るに足らない情報という“ノイズ”と，重要な出来事という“信号”を何らかの方法で区別しなければならない。

私たちは，睡眠中の脳内でのニューロンの自発発火が，新たな記憶痕跡と以前に学習ずみのさまざまなネットワークの両方を含む多種多様な神経回路を，多種多様な組み合わせで活性化するのだと考えている。夢が時として支離滅裂なのはこの神経的混乱状態の反映だ。この自発的な活動は，新しい記憶のうちどれが保存ずみの重要な記憶とよりよく合致するかを脳に試させ，うまく合致しないものを弱める。私たちを含めいくつかの研究グループは，脳の活動が“信号”に対応するシナプスを維持しつつ，“ノイズ”を符号化するシナプスを選択的に弱めるようなメカニズムを探っている。

脳がこのような仮想的なシナリオを試して，適宜シナプスを弱める作業を進めている間は，我々自身は周囲の環境を意識せずじっとしているのがよい。つまり，眠っているのが一番よいのだ。また，シナプス恒常性の回復は覚醒時には起こらないはずだ。なぜなら，覚醒時にはその日の出来事の処理が主体になっているから，過去に蓄積した知識の総体と対照している余裕はないからだ。睡眠がもたらす完全な遮断状態は，目下起きていることの支配から脳を解放し，記憶を整理統合するのに最適の状況を生み出す。

Giulio Tononi ／ Chiara Cirelli
ともに米ウィスコンシン大学マディソン校教授。睡眠の機能に関する彼らの研究は，トノーニの著書である“Phi: A Voyage from the Brain to the Soul”（Pantheon，2012）のテーマとなっている，人間の意識についてのより広範な研究の一環をなす。

Proust among the Machines

機械は意識を持ちうるか

C. コッホ
（米アレン脳科学研究所）

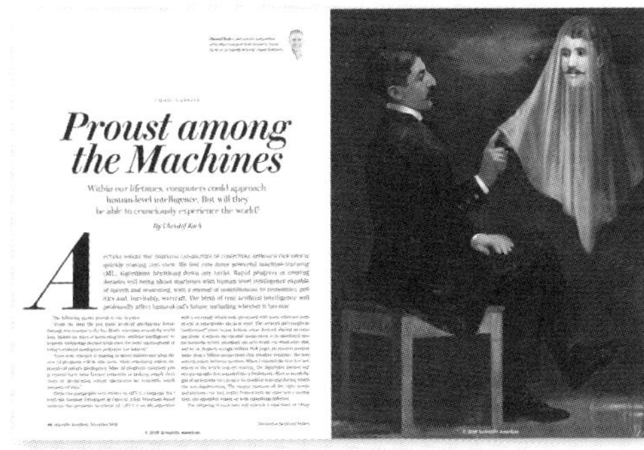

Proust among the Machines

Within our lifetimes, computers could approach human-level intelligence. But will they be able to consciously experience the world?

By Christof Koch

私たちが生きているうちにコンピューターは
人間並みの知能に近づく可能性がある
だが，それらは世界を意識的に体験できるだろうか

KEY CONCEPTS

シミュレーションでは解けない謎

■人間と同レベルの知能を備えた機械の実現が近づいてきた。

■だが，それらが意識を持つかどうかは，依然としてわからないだろう。

■その理由は？　脳を最も精巧にシミュレーションしても，意識的な知覚が生じる見込みは薄いからだ。

日経サイエンス 2020 年 3 月号，SCIENTIFIC AMERICAN December 2019

A future where the thinking capabilities of computers approach our own is quickly coming into view. We feel ever more powerful machine-learning (ML) algorithms breathing down our necks. Rapid progress in coming decades will bring about machines with human-level intelligence capable of speech and reasoning, with a myriad of contributions to economics, politics and, inevitably, warcraft. The birth of true artificial intelligence will profoundly affect humankind's future, including whether it has one.

The following quotes provide a case in point:

"From the time the last great artificial intelligence breakthrough was reached in the late 1940s, scientists around the world have looked for ways of harnessing this 'artificial intelligence' to improve technology beyond what even the most sophisticated of today's artificial intelligence programs can achieve."

"Even now, research is ongoing to better understand what the new AI programs will be able to do, while remaining within the bounds of today's intelligence. Most AI programs currently programmed have been limited primarily to making simple decisions or performing simple operations on relatively small amounts of data."

These two paragraphs were written by GPT-2, a language bot I tried last summer. Developed by OpenAI, a San Francisco–based institute that promotes beneficial AI, GPT-2 is an ML algorithm with a seemingly idiotic task: presented with some arbitrary starter text, it must predict the next word. The network isn't taught to "understand" prose in any human sense. Instead, during its training phase, it adjusts the internal connections in its simulated neural networks to best anticipate the next word, the word after that, and so on. Trained on eight million Web pages, its innards contain more than a billion connections that

Vocabulary

[タイトル] **Proust** マルセル・プルースト
▶この記事の読み方

thinking capabilities 思考能力
come into view 視野に入る
ever more これまで以上に
machine learning 機械学習
breathe down someone's neck しつこくつきまとう, 絶えず監視する
coming decades 今後数十年
bring about もたらす
speech 発話, 言葉を話すこと
reasoning 推論
a myriad of 無数の, 数え切れないほどの
inevitably 避けがたいことに
warcraft 戦争遂行技術
artificial intelligence 人工知能
profoundly 大きく

quote 引用文
case in point よい例

reach 達成する
harness 活用する

ongoing 進行中で
within the bounds of ～の範囲内に
programmed 計画された
operation 演算, 操作

language bot 言語ボット
beneficial 役に立つ
seemingly 一見
idiotic ばかばかしい
present with ～を提示する
arbitrary 任意の
starter text 出発点となる文
prose 散文, 文
internal connection 内的接続
neural network 神経ネットワーク, ニューラルネット
innards 内部組織

emulate synapses, the connecting points between neurons. When I entered the first few sentences of the article you are reading, the algorithm spewed out two paragraphs that sounded like a freshman's effort to recall the gist of an introductory lecture on machine learning during which she was daydreaming. The output contains all the right words and phrases—not bad, really! Primed with the same text a second time, the algorithm comes up with something different.

The offspring of such bots will unleash a tidal wave of "deepfake" product reviews and news stories that will add to the miasma of the Internet. They will become just one more example of programs that do things hitherto thought to be uniquely human—playing the real-time strategy game StarCraft, translating text, making personal recommendations for books and movies, recognizing people in images and videos.

It will take many further advances in machine learning before an algorithm can write a masterpiece as coherent as Marcel Proust's In Search of Lost Time, but the code is on the wall. Recall that all early attempts at computer game playing, translation and speech were clumsy and easy to belittle because they so obviously lacked skill and polish. But with the invention of deep neural networks and the massive computational infrastructure of the tech industry, computers relentlessly improved until their outputs no longer appeared risible. As we have seen with Go, chess and poker, today's algorithms can best humans, and when they do, our initial laughter turns to consternation. Are we like Goethe's sorcerer's apprentice, having summoned helpful spirits that we now are unable to control?

Artificial Consciousness?

Although experts disagree over what exactly constitutes intelligence, natural or otherwise, most accept that, sooner or later, computers will achieve what is termed artificial general intelligence (AGI) in the lingo.

Vocabulary

emulate 模する
synapse シナプス
spew out 吐き出す
freshman 大学1年生
gist 要旨
daydream 空想にふける，ボーッとする
primed with ～を与えられる
come up with 考え出す

offspring 子孫
unleash 解き放つ
tidal wave 高波，うねり
deep-fake ディープフェイク
add to ～を増大させる
miasma 毒気
hitherto これまで

coherent 理路整然とした
the code is on the wall 不吉な前兆がある（慣用句 **the writing is on the wall** のもじり）
clumsy 不器用な，ぎこちない
belittle 見くびる
polish 洗練
relentlessly 絶え間なく
risible 笑ってしまうような，噴飯ものの
best ～に勝つ，～を負かす
consternation 狼狽
sorcerer's apprentice 「魔法使いの弟子」
summon 呼び出す

artificial consciousness 人工意識
▶この記事の読み方
sooner or later 遅かれ早かれ
artificial general intelligence（AGI） 汎用人工知能
lingo 専門用語

The focus on machine intelligence obscures quite different questions: Will it feel like anything to be an AGI? Can programmable computers ever be conscious?

By "consciousness" or "subjective feeling," I mean the quality inherent in any one experience—for instance, the delectable taste of Nutella, the sharp sting of an infected tooth, the slow passage of time when one is bored, or the sense of vitality and anxiety just before a competitive event. Channeling philosopher Thomas Nagel, we could say a system is conscious if there is something it is like to be that system.

Consider the embarrassing feeling of suddenly realizing that you have just committed a gaffe, that what you meant as a joke came across as an insult. Can computers ever experience such roiling emotions? When you are on the phone, waiting minute after minute, and a synthetic voice intones, "We are sorry to keep you waiting," does the software actually feel bad while keeping you in customer-service hell?

There is little doubt that our intelligence and our experiences are ineluctable consequences of the natural causal powers of our brain, rather than any supernatural ones. That premise has served science extremely well over the past few centuries as people explored the world. The three-pound, tofulike human brain is by far the most complex chunk of organized active matter in the known universe. But it has to obey the same physical laws as dogs, trees and stars. Nothing gets a free pass. We do not yet fully understand the brain's causal powers, but we experience them every day—one group of neurons is active while you are seeing colors, whereas the cells firing in another cortical neighborhood are associated with being in a jocular mood. When these neurons are stimulated by a neurosurgeon's electrode, the subject sees colors or erupts in laughter. Conversely, shutting down the brain during anesthesia elimi-

Vocabulary

obscure 曖昧にする，見えにくくする

subjective feeling 主観的感覚
inherent 本質的に備わっている
delectable おいしい
sting チクチクする痛み
channel ～とチャネリングする，～流に表現する

embarrassing ばつの悪い，間の悪い
gaffe 失言
come across as ～と受け取られる
insult 侮辱
roiling 心をかき乱す，どぎまぎした
intone 唱えるように言う
feel bad 申し訳ないと感じる

ineluctable 避けられない
causal power 因果的効力
▶この記事の読み方
premise 前提
chunk 塊
active matter 活性物質
physical laws 物理法則
fire 発火する
cortical 皮質の
jocular おどけた
neurosurgeon 神経外科医
electrode 電極
subject 被験者
erupt in laughter いきなり笑い出す
conversely 逆に，反対に
anesthesia 麻酔

nates these experiences.

Given these widely shared background assumptions, what will the evolution of true artificial intelligence imply about the possibility of artificial consciousness?

Contemplating this question, we inevitably come to a fork up ahead, leading to two fundamentally different destinations. The zeitgeist, as embodied in novels and movies such as Blade Runner, Her and Ex Machina, marches resolutely down the road toward the assumption that truly intelligent machines will be sentient; they will speak, reason, self-monitor and introspect. They are eo ipso conscious.

This path is epitomized most explicitly by the global neuronal workspace (GNW) theory, one of the dominant scientific theories of consciousness. The theory starts with the brain and infers that some of its peculiar architectural features are what gives rise to consciousness.

Its lineage can be traced back to the "blackboard architecture" of 1970s computer science, in which specialized programs accessed a shared repository of information, called the blackboard or central workspace. Psychologists postulated that such a processing resource exists in the brain and is central to human cognition. Its capacity is small, so only a single percept, thought or memory occupies the workspace at any one time. New information competes with the old and displaces it.

Cognitive neuroscientist Stanislas Dehaene and molecular biologist Jean-Pierre Changeux, both at the Collège de France in Paris, mapped these ideas onto the architecture of the brain's cortex, the outermost layer of gray matter. Two highly folded cortical sheets, one on the left and one on the right, each the size and thickness of a 14-inch pizza, are crammed into the protective skull. Dehaene

Vocabulary

given ～を考えると，～を踏まえると
evolution 進化
imply 意味する，暗示する

contemplate 熟考する，考える
inevitably 必然的に
fork 分岐点
up ahead 先にある
zeitgeist 時代精神
resolutely 断固として
sentient 意識を持つ
reason 推論する
introspect 内省する
eo ipso そのこと自体によって

epitomize 象徴する
explicitly はっきりと
dominant 有力な
infer 推測する
peculiar architectural features 特有の情報処理構造の特徴
give rise to 生じさせる

lineage (考え方の)血統，系統
blackboard architecture 黒板モデル
repository 貯蔵庫
postulate 仮定する，想定する
cognition 認知
percept 知覚(されるもの)
displace ～に置き換わる

cognitive neuroscientist 認知神経科学者
map 対応づける
cortex 皮質
gray matte 灰白質
folded 折りたたまれた
cortical sheet 皮質シート
cram 詰め込む

and Changeux postulated that the workspace is instantiated by a network of pyramidal (excitatory) neurons linked to far-flung cortical regions, in particular the prefrontal, parietotemporal and midline (cingulate) associative areas.

Much brain activity remains localized and therefore unconscious—for example, that of the module that controls where the eyes look, something of which we are almost completely oblivious, or that of the module that adjusts the posture of our bodies. But when activity in one or more regions exceeds a threshold—say, when someone is presented with an image of a Nutella jar—it triggers an ignition, a wave of neural excitation that spreads throughout the neuronal workspace, brain-wide. That signaling therefore becomes available to a host of subsidiary processes such as language, planning, reward circuits, access to long-term memory, and storage in a short-term memory buffer. The act of globally broadcasting this information is what renders it conscious. The inimitable experience of Nutella is constituted by pyramidal neurons contacting the brain's motor-planning region—issuing an instruction to grab a spoon to scoop out some of the hazelnut spread. Meanwhile other modules transmit the message to expect a reward in the form of a dopamine rush caused by Nutella's high fat and sugar content.

Conscious states arise from the way the workspace algorithm processes the relevant sensory inputs, motor outputs, and internal variables related to memory, motivation and expectation. Global processing is what consciousness is about. GNW theory fully embraces the contemporary mythos of the near-infinite powers of computation. Consciousness is just a clever hack away.

Vocabulary

instantiate 実体化する
pyramidal (excitatory) neuron 錐体(興奮性)ニューロン
far-flung 遠く離れた
prefrontal associative area 前頭連合野
parieto-temporal associative area 頭頂側頭連合野
midline (cingulate) associative area 正中(帯状)連合野

localized 局所的な, 局在的な
oblivious 気づかない
posture 姿勢
threshold 閾値
say 例えば
jar 瓶
ignition 発火
neural excitation 神経の興奮
subsidiary processes 副次的過程
long-term memory 長期記憶
short-term memory 短期記憶
globally 脳全体に
broadcast 広める
render ～にする
inimitable まねできない, 比類のない
motor-planning region 行動計画(運動プランニング)領域

internal variable 内的変数
embrace 支持する
mythos 神話
hack 力わざ, こつ, 解決法

コンピューターの思考能力が人間に近づく未来が急速に視野に入ってきた。ますます強力な機械学習アルゴリズムが背後に迫っているのを私たちは実感している。今後数十年の急速な技術進歩によって，言葉を話し推論できる人間並みの知能を備えた機械が実現し，経済や政治，そして避けがたいことに兵器にも，多面的に寄与するだろう。真の人工知能（AI）の誕生は人類の未来を大きく左右するだろう。人類が未来を持ちうるかどうかを含めて。

次の引用文がよい例だ。

「最近の大きな人工知能ブレークスルーが達成された1940年代後半以来，世界中の科学者はこの『人工知能』を活用して，技術を今日の最も精巧な人工知能プログラムが達成可能な水準さえも超えて改善する方法を探してきた。」

「新たなＡＩプログラムによってなにが可能になるかを理解しようとする研究が進行中であり，一方でそれは現在の知能の範囲内ににとどまっている。現在プログラムされているAIプログラムの大半は，主に簡単な決定をすることと，比較的少量のデータについて簡単な操作を実行することに限られている。」

以上2つの文章は，昨年の夏に私が試しに言語ボット「GPT-2」に書かせたものだ。GPT-2は実用的なAIの開発に力を入れているサンフランシスコの非営利団体オープンAIが開発した機械学習アルゴリズムで，やっていることは一見すると単純だ。与えられた任意の文を出発点にして，次に来る単語を予測する。このニューラルネットは人間のように文を“理解”するようには教えられていない。そうではなく，次の単語として最適なものを予測し，その単語の次に来る最適な単語を予測するという操作を繰り返し実行できるように，学習訓練を通じてニューラルネットの内部接続を調節する。800万のウェブページで訓練したことで，シナプス（脳のニューロンの接続点）を模した10億個を超える接続を内包している。あなたが読んでいるこの記事の冒頭の数行を入力した結果として，このアルゴリズムが吐き出したのが上の2つの文章だ。機械学習の入門講座をぼーっと聞いていた大学 1 年生が講義の要旨を思い出して書いたような文章だ。単語と語法はすべて正しく，実際そう悪くない。次に再度同じ文を出発点として与えたら，少し違った文章が出てくるだろう。

将来はこうしたボットの子孫によって“ディープフェイク”の商品レビューやニュース記事が大量にウェブ上に解き放たれ，インターネットの毒気はさらにひどくなるだろう。これも，それまで人間だけが行うと考えられていたことをコンピューターが実行するようになる一例にすぎない。コンピューターはすでに，リアルタイム戦略ゲーム『スタークラフト』のプレイや文章の翻訳，お好みの書籍や映画の推薦，画像中の人物認識などをこなしている。

アルゴリズムがプルースト（Marcel Proust）の『失われた時を求めて』のような傑作を書けるようになるには機械学習の多大な進歩が必要だろうが，見くびるわけにもいかない。ゲームのプレイや翻訳，発話などコンピューターが挑んだ初期の試みは明らかに不器用でお粗末な出来だったが，ディープニューラルネットワークの発明とハイテク産業の強大な計算インフラによって，コンピューターの性能は絶え間なく向上を続け，それが出力する結果はもはや馬鹿にできないものになった。囲碁やチェス，ポーカーで示されたように，現在のアルゴリズムは人間を打ち負かすことができ，そうなると当初の嘲笑は狼狽に変わる。私たちはゲーテの「魔法使いの弟子」のように，役に立つが制御不能なものを呼び出してしまったのだろうか？

人工意識？

何が知能を構成しているのかに関して専門家の見解は分かれているものの，コンピューターが遅かれ早かれ専門用語で「汎用人工知能（AGI）」と呼ばれるものを達成するだろうという点では見解がほぼ一致している。

機械知能に関しては，それとはかなり異質でわかりにくい疑問がある。そうした AI は自分が汎用人工知能であるという自覚を持つのか？　プログラム可能なコンピューターは意識を持ちうるのか？

ここで私がいう「意識」あるいは「主観的感覚」とは，あらゆる体験がそれぞれ本来的に備えている特質を意味している。例えばチョコレート風味ナッツバター「ヌテラ」の甘くておいしい味や，虫歯の刺すような痛み，退屈しているときの遅い時間経過，競技を前にした武者震いや不安の感覚などだ。「コウモリであるとはどのようなことか」を論じた哲学者のネーゲル（Thomas Nagel）流に表現すれば，あるシステムがそのシステムらしい何かを備えているのなら，そのシステムは意識を持つといえるだろう。

冗談で言ったことが相手から侮辱と受け止められ，失言だったと気づいたときの間の悪い感覚を考えよう。コンピューターはこの種のどぎまぎした感情を体験しうるだろうか？　どこかのお客様相談室に電話したものの何分も待た

この記事の読み方

記事の原題は “Proust among the Machines”。フランスの作家プルーストは『失われた時を求めて』という長大な小説を書いたが，機械もこれに並ぶような小説が書けるようになるかという問いである。邦題のほうは artificial consciousness（人工意識）に力点をおいた題に変えられている。

AI 関連の用語が頻出するが，それらに慣れている人には，さほど難しい文章ではないだろう。脳の causal power（因果的効力）という表現が出てくるが，これは脳が活動することによって感覚（意識）体験が引き起こされることを指している。もし機械もそれと同じように活動するなら，感覚体験，すなわち人工意識を生み出せるのではないか。記事の後半では，グローバル・ワークスペース理論や統合情報理論といった意識理論の点から，その可能性を探っている。

記事の掲載年は 2019 年。ここで登場した GPT-2 はバージョンアップされて，2022 年に ChatGPT として公開された。この画期的な生成 AI が出現して以降，機械が人間のような知性や意識を持ちうるかという議論は，次の局面を迎えている。

され，合成音声の「お待たせして申し訳ございません」という単調なメッセージが繰り返されるとき，このソフトウエアは本当に申し訳ないと感じているのだろうか？

人間の知能と体験をもたらしているのが超自然的な何かではなく，脳が本来備えている因果的効力の不可避的な結果であることに疑問の余地はまずない。過去数百年にわたる科学的探求のなかで，この前提は非常によく通用してきた。重さ 1.4kg の豆腐のような人間の脳は，既知の宇宙のなかで最も複雑に組織された活性物質の塊だ。だが，この脳も犬や樹木，星が従っているのと同じ物理法則に従わねばならない。これを免除されるものは存在しない。脳の因果的効力はまだ完全には理解されていないが，私たちはそれを毎日体験している。色を見ているときにはあるグループのニューロンが活動し，冗談気分でいるときには別の皮質領域の脳細胞が発火する。外科的に挿入した電極でこれらのニューロンを刺激すると，その被験者は色が見えたり，吹き出し笑いをしたりする。反対に，麻酔によって脳を休業させると，こうした体験は消える。

これら広く受け入れられてきた前提を踏まえた場合，真の人工知能の進化は人工意識の実現可能性にどんな意味を持つだろうか？

この問題を考えていくと，根本的に異なる 2 つの場所につながる分岐点に至る。一方の道は，真に知的な機械は意識を備えたものになるという結論につながるものだ。『ブレードランナー』や『her／世界でひとつの彼女』『エクス・マキナ』などの小説や映画が体現しているように，現在の時代精神は明らかにこの道を進んでいる。それらの知的機械は言葉を話し，推論し，自己をモニタリングし，内省する。事実上，これらは意識を持っている。

この道筋を最も明示的に表す仮説が，意識に関する有力な科学理論の 1 つである「グローバル・ワークスペース理論」だ。この理論は脳を出発点とし，脳特有の情報処理構造の特徴から意識が生じてくると考える。

このような考え方は1970年代のコンピューター科学が生んだ「黒板モデル」にさかのぼる。それぞれに専門化したプログラムが共通の情報貯蔵庫（「黒板」もしくは「中央作業空間」と呼ばれる）にアクセスする構造だ。心理学者はこれと同様の情報処理機構が人間の脳に存在し，認知の中核を担っていると考えた。ただし，この作業空間は小さいので，そこに収容できる知覚や思考，記憶はどの時点でも1つだけだ。新たな情報がやってくると古い情報と競い合い，作業空間で古い情報に置き換わる。

パリにあるコレージュ・ド・フランスの神経科学者ドゥアンヌ（Stanislas Dehaene）と分子生物学者シャンジュー（Jean-Pierre Changeux）は，この考えを脳の皮質（灰白質の最外層）の構造に対応づけた。皮質シートは脳の左右の半球に分かれ，それぞれ14インチのピザと同程度の大きさと厚さで，それが折りたたまれて頭蓋骨に収まっている。ドゥアンヌとシャンジューは，脳の作業空間（ワークスペース）の実体が離れた皮質領域を結ぶニューロンのネットワークであると考えた。特に前頭連合野と頭頂側頭連合野，正中（帯状）連合野を結ぶネットワークだ。

脳の活動の多くは局所にとどまり，このため意識に上らない。例えば目をどこに向けるかを制御するモジュールや体の姿勢を調節するモジュールの活動がこれで，私たちはそれらの活動にほぼ完全に気づいていない。だが，1つあるいは複数の脳領域の活動がある閾値を超えると（例えばヌテラの瓶を見ると），それをきっかけにニューロンが発火し，神経的興奮の波が脳全体にわたる神経作業空間の隅々に広がる。この信号は言語処理や計画，報酬回路，長期記憶へのアクセス，短期記憶の貯蔵など，多数の副次的過程に利用可能となる。情報を脳全体に広めるこの活動が，脳に意識を付与する。ヌテラに関する独特の体験は，脳の行動計画領域（スプーンを手に取ってナッツバターをすくい取る指令を出す領域）と接続しているニューロンによって生じる。一方，他のモジュールはこの情報をもとに，脂肪と糖に富むヌテラがドーパミン放出の形でもたらす報酬を予測する。

関連の感覚入力と運動出力，そして記憶や意欲，期待に関する内的変数を作業空間でアルゴリズムが処理する仕方から，意識状態が生まれる。このグローバルな処理が意識の本質だ。グローバル・ワークスペース理論はコンピューターの無限に近いパワーという現代の神話を全面的に支持する。巧みな力わざさえあれば，意識は生じる。

Christof Koch
米シアトルにあるアレン脳科学研究所の首席科学者・社長。SCIENTIFIC AMERICAN 誌の編集顧問でもある。

心の発達

2

Our Stuff, Ourselves

愛着の心理学

Age of Opportunity

反抗期の脳とうまく向き合うには

Baby Talk

赤ちゃんの超言語力

Our Stuff, Ourselves

愛着の心理学

F. ルッソ
（ジャーナリスト）

私たちは精神的に不安定になると
所有物との関わりを強めようとすることがある

KEY CONCEPTS

人間と安心感と所有物の複雑な関係

■人間は社会的動物だ。私たちが精神的に安心するには，強い自我と他者との関係における自信が必要だ。

■大切な人への愛着が不安定な場合，生命のない所有物に深い意味や人間的な特性を与えて，その空白を埋めようとすることがある。

■物理的接触を通じて自分のエッセンスが所有物に吹き込まれるとともに，他者の所有物に触れるとその人のエッセンスを取り込むことになると信じている人もいるようだ。

■大切な所有物の擬人化は正常なことだ。だが，溜め込みという病的な状態になることもある。

日経サイエンス 2018 年 10 月号，SCIENTIFIC AMERICAN May 2018

In a colorfully decorated classroom, a five-year-old boy is asked to describe his favorite belonging. He talks effusively about the dinosaur T-shirt his mom forced him to put in the wash that morning. Then he plays two simple computer games, trying, of course, to win. But the fix is in: experimenters have arranged that he will win one game and lose the other (and, to avoid suffering harm, will win a third and final game at the experiment's end). After winning and after losing, he, like the other boys and girls in this 2015 study conducted by psychologist Gil Diesendruck of Bar-Ilan University in Israel and his colleague, is asked by an adult whether he would be willing to lend this favorite thing to another child for one night.

This experiment set out to explore whether injury to young children's sense of self resulted in a stronger attachment to personally meaningful possessions. The results were dramatic. Children were almost twice as likely to be willing to share their most treasured belonging after winning the game than after losing. Yet in a control situation involving possessions they cared less about, the children's success or failure in the games had no effect on their willingness to part with the items.

Such experiments are among the latest efforts to understand the deeply emotional and psychologically complex relationship between humans, their sense of security and their material possessions. Much of this new research builds on the late 20th-century work of pioneering psychologists John Bowlby, Mary Ainsworth and Donald Winnicott. They famously theorized that an infant's attachment to his or her mother and the quality of that attachment significantly influenced that child's future relationships. Winnicott also suggested that as an infant begins to perceive that he or she has an independent self that is separate from the mother, that infant can learn to feel more secure with a "transitional object" that stands in for her. In popular parlance, we call this a "security blanket."

Vocabulary

［タイトル］ **stuff** 物，所有物
▶この記事の読み方

belonging 持ち物，所有物
effusively 熱っぽく
wash 洗濯物
the fix is in 不正工作がなされている，仕組まれている
colleague 共同研究者
challenge 難題
loom 不気味に迫る

set out 目指す
Injury 傷
sense of self 自意識
attachment 愛着
▶この記事の読み方
possessions 所有物
treasured 大切な
control 対照
part with 手放す

sense of security 安心感
material possessions 物質的所有物
build on ～を基礎とする，踏まえる
perceive 知覚する，認識する
self 自我
secure 安心な
transitional object 移行対象
▶この記事の読み方
stand in for ～の代わりとなる
parlance 用語
security blanket 安心毛布
▶この記事の読み方

Since then, other branches of science, from evolutionary psychology and anthropology to consumer research and neuroscience, have affirmed that our belongings fill many emotional needs. They comfort us amid loneliness and boost our confidence about our abilities. In fact, our possessions do not just make us feel secure by substituting for important people in our lives; we actually see these objects as an extension of ourselves. We believe—or perhaps act as if we believe—that in some way, our very essence permeates our things. If these things become damaged or lost, we ourselves feel damaged or lost.

Stated baldly, our relationship with our stuff can sound a little crazy. But it is perfectly normal. "We all keep things and take great comfort in our possessions," says Nick Neave, an evolutionary psychologist at Northumbria University in England. "It's part of our evolutionary heritage." Keeping food—especially if it was hard to get—was and still is a major survival mechanism, Neave explains. The same is true of weapons and tools. "If you send someone into the world with nothing," he says, "they feel vulnerable. They need their possessions to make survival possible."

Human beings are, of course, social animals, so our needs for security are more complex than just the basics for physical survival. It may be helpful to recall psychologist Abraham Maslow's classic hierarchy of needs, expressed visually as a pyramid. Published in 1943, the pyramid's large base represents physiological needs (food, air and water), then builds upward through layers of physical safety (shelter, weapons), love and belonging (relationships and community) to esteem (ego strength) and, at its peak, self-actualization (optimal emotional health in which we realize our full potential). With the possible exception of self-actualization, our belongings can play a role in affording security in all these areas, including ego security and confidence in our relationships.

Vocabulary

evolutionary psychology 進化心理学
anthropology 人類学
neuroscience 神経科学
affirm 確認する
emotional needs 感情的ニーズ, 情動的欲求
substitute for ～の代わりにする
extension 延長
permeate ～に染み込む

baldly あからさまに, 端的に
take great comfort in ～に大いに慰められる
true 当てはまる
vulnerable 無防備な

hierarchy of needs 欲求の階層(欲求ピラミッド)
physiological needs 生理的欲求
physical safety 身体的な安全
shelter 隠れ家
belonging 所属
esteem 承認
self-actualization 自己実現
play a role 一役買う
afford もたらす

Theories of Attachment

Can you name your so-called attachment style? Probably not, unless you have had psychoanalysis. The psychoanalytic literature has identified four major attachment categories. If as a small child, you felt that your caregiver was reliably present and dependably met your needs, you developed a secure attachment style. But if your caregiver pushed you away in times of need, you probably developed attachment avoidance, learning to be independent and emotionally distant. Meanwhile if you perceived that your caregiver was inconsistent in meeting your needs, you may have developed an anxious attachment style, where you cling to or are constantly monitoring people in your intimate circle to make sure they will be there for you. Those who felt harmed in some way by their caregivers in early childhood develop a fearful/avoidant attachment style, making them afraid to get close to others. A classic American study in 1987 by researchers Cindy Hazan and Phillip Shaver, both then at the University of Denver, found that 56 percent of us have a secure attachment style, about 20 percent are anxious and about 24 percent are avoidant.

Vocabulary

attachment style 愛着スタイル
 ▶この記事の読み方
psychoanalysis 精神分析
literature 文献
caregiver 養育者
secure 安定の, 安全な
avoidance 回避
push someone away 突き放す
distant 距離をおいた
inconsistent 一貫性がない
anxious 不安な
cling to ～にしがみつく
fearful 恐ろしい
avoidant 回避性の

By drawing on this early psychoanalytic work, scientists have recently created provocative experiments that are beginning to nail down the roles various attachment styles play in our love affair with our things. Notably, anxious and other insecure attachment styles may be on the rise. A 2014 meta-analysis of studies involving American college students found that the percentage of students who scored as having secure attachment decreased from about 49 percent in 1988 to about 42 percent in 2011. The authors speculated on explanations or correlations, including reported increases in individualism, narcissism and materialism.

provocative 挑発的な
nail down 明らかにする
notably 注目すべきことに
insecure 不安定な
on the rise 増えている
speculate on ～について考える
correlation 相関

As more people suffer from insecure attachment styles, the behavior of seeking emotional solace from material objects is likely rising, too. According to an intriguing three-part study by psychologist Lucas A. Keefer, now at the Univer-

solace 癒やし
material object 形ある物
intriguing 興味深い

sity of Southern Mississippi, and his colleagues, people cling more tightly to their belongings when they feel less confident about the people they care for. In this research, published in 2012 in the Journal of Experimental Social Psychology, the first participants were randomly asked to write about three recent instances when someone close to them had let them down. Subjects in a second group either wrote about when a stranger had let them down or when they had let themselves down. Only people in the first group—primed to consider the unreliability of their close friends or romantic partners—reported greater uncertainty that they could count on others and an increased attachment to objects.

In the third part of the study, undergraduates were asked to write a few sentences either on uncertainties they felt about their abilities or uncertainties they felt about their relationships. Then the experimenter asked all the participants to relinquish their cell phone, which would be returned as soon as they completed an open-ended writing assignment. Keefer found that those asked to write about uncertainties regarding their relationships reported greater separation anxiety from their phone and showed (by how fast they finished the writing task) a more urgent need to get it back. This was true even when the researchers controlled for the phone's perceived usefulness as a social tool.

Why do we reach for things when people we care about let us down? That worn sweatshirt is not human. It does not show us compassion. Neither does a teddy bear or a coffee mug. But, scientists point out, these objects are utterly reliable, always present and under our control. We can count on them.

Vocabulary

confident about ～を信頼する
care for 大切に思っている
participant 被験者，実験参加者
instance 出来事
someone close to them 身近な人
let someone down 失望させる
stranger 知らない人
let oneself down 落ちこむ
primed to ～するよう事前に言われる
unreliability 不信感

undergraduate 大学生，学部生
uncertainty 不安
relinquish 手放す
open-ended 時間制限なしの
writing assignment 作文課題
separation anxiety 手放すことに対する不安
urgent 差し迫った

care about 大切に思う
worn 着古した
compassion 同情
utterly すっかり，完全に
count on 頼りにする

カラフルに装飾された教室で，5歳の男の子がお気に入りの持ち物について話すよう求められた。彼は，今朝母親に言われて渋々洗濯機に入れた恐竜柄のTシャツについて熱っぽく語った。その後，2つの簡単なコンピューターゲームをした。もちろん勝とうとしたのだが，ゲームは仕組まれており，1つのゲームでは勝ち，もう1つのゲームでは負けるようになっていた（悪影響を避けるため，実験の最後に用意した3つ目のゲームでは男の子が勝つようにしてあった）。勝った後と負けた後のそれぞれで，男の子はお気に入りのTシャツを別の子どもに一晩貸してもよいかと尋ねられた。

これはイスラエルのバル＝イラン大学の心理学者ディーセンドラック（Gil Diesendruck）らが2015年に行った実験で，他の子どもたちも同様の質問を受けた。この実験の目的は，子どもが自意識を傷つけられると，大切に思っている所有物への愛着を強めるかどうかを調べることにあった。結果は目を見張るものだった。最も大切な所有物を他人に貸してもよいと子どもが答える確率は，ゲームに勝った後では負けた後の約2倍だった。これに対し，それほど大切でない所有物の場合には，ゲームの勝敗は判断に何の影響も及ぼさなかった。

こうした実験は，人間と安心感と物質的所有物の間にある感情に関わる心理学的にも複雑な関係を解明しようとする最近の取り組みの1つだ。これらの新たな研究は，先駆的な心理学者のボウルビィ（John Bowlby）やエインスワース（Mary Ainsworth），ウィニコット（Donald Winnicott）が20世紀後半に行った研究に端を発している。彼らは，幼児の母親への愛着とその愛着の質がその子の将来の人間関係に大きく影響するという仮説で有名だ。ウィニコットはまた，幼児は自分が母親とは別の独立した自我を持っていることを認識し始めると，母親の代わりとなる「移行対象」によって安心感を高めるようになると主張した。平たくいえば「安心毛布」のことだ。

以来，進化心理学や人類学，消費者行動研究，神経科学といった他の分野でも，所有物がさまざまな感情的ニーズを満たしてくれることが確認されてきた。所有物は寂しいときに慰めとなったり，自分の能力に対する自信を強めてくれたりする。さらに，所有物は大切な人の代わりとして安心感を与えてくれるだけではない。私たちは実際に所有物を自分自身の延長とみなしている。つまり，自分のエッセンスが所有物に何らかの形で染み込んでいると信じている，あるいはそう信じているように行動する。それらの所有物が傷つけられたり失われたりすると，自分も傷ついたり喪失感を味わったりする。

端的に言えば，所有物とのこの関係は奇妙に思える。だが，それはまったく正常なことだ。「人はみな物を所有しているし，所有物に大いに慰められている」と，英ノーザンブリア大学の進化心理学者ニーブ（Nick Neave）は言う。「これは進化の過程で受け継いできたものだ」。食物（特にようやく手に入れたもの）を取っておくことは，今でも重要な生存方法だとニーブは説明する。同じことが武器や道具にも当てはまる。「人は何も持たずに世の中に放り出されると無防備に感じる」と彼は言う。「生き延びることを可能にする所有物が必要なのだ」。

もちろん人間は社会的な動物なので，安心感を得るために必要となるものは，単に生存を可能にする基本的な事柄よりもずっと複雑だ。その説明には，心理学者マズロー（Abraham Maslow）の有名な「欲求の階層（欲求ピラミッド）」が役立つだろう。1943 年に発表された欲求ピラミッドでは，生理的欲求（食物や空気，水）が底辺を占め，その上に身体的な安全（隠れ家や武器），愛と所属（人間関係や社会），承認（強い自我）の各欲求が順に積み重なり，自己実現の欲求（自分の能力を最大限に発揮している情緒的に最適な健康状態）が頂点を占める。自己実現はともかく，自己の安全や人間関係における自信といったこれらすべての領域で，所有物は安心感をもたらすのに一役買っている。

愛着の理論

あなたは自分のいわゆる「愛着スタイル」を知っているだろうか？　精神分析を受けたことがなければ知らないだろう。精神分析に関する文献によると，愛着スタイルは主に 4 種類ある。まず，幼児期に養育者が確実にそばにいて自分の欲求を誠実に満たしてくれると感じていた人は，「安定型」の愛着スタイルを形成している。だが，必要なときに養育者に突き放された経験がある人は，自立して感情的に距離をおく「回避型」の愛着スタイルを形成しているだろう。また，養育者が自分の欲求を満たしてくれるとは限らないと気付いた人は「不安型」の愛着スタイルを形成し，親しい人が確実にそばにいてもらえるよう，その人にしがみついたり常に監視したりするだろう。最後に，幼少期に養育者に何らかの形で傷つけられたと感じた人は，「恐れ／回避型」の愛着スタイルを形成し，他者と親しくなるのを恐れるようになる。1987 年に当時デンバー大学にいたハザン（Cindy Hazan）とシェイバー（Phillip Shaver）が米国で行った有名な研究では，56%の人が安定型，20%が不安型，24%が回避型の愛着スタイルだった。

この初期の精神分析的研究を参考にして最近行われた実験から，さまざまな愛着スタイルが所有物への愛着にどう影響しているかが明らかになりつつある。注目すべきことに，不安型など不安定な愛着スタイルの人が増えている可能性がある。米国の大学生を対象に行われた研究を 2014 年にメタ分析した結果，安定型の愛着スタイルと判定された学生の割合は 1988 年の約 49%から 2011 年には約 42%に減少していた。この分析を行った研究者たちはその結果について，近年報告されている個人主義や自己愛，物質主義の高まりが関係しているのでは

この記事の読み方

attachment（愛着）は，20 世紀半ばボウルビィによって提唱された概念。子どもと養育者の間に形成される情緒的な絆（結びつき）のことを指す。attach の tach は touch（接触／感触）と同義。したがって，attachment は両者間の心理的結びつきだけでなく，physical contact（物理的／身体的接触）も含意している。

記事は，愛着の対象が人間や動物だけでなく，無生物のモノにも拡張され，自分の所有物が自己アイデンティティの一部にもなりうると論じている。最後では，病的な愛着の例として，溜め込み症候群についても触れている。

掲載文では，愛着の概念とモノへの愛着について述べたあと，attachment style（愛着スタイル）と所有物への愛着の関係について述べている。なお，ウィニコットは，子どもの愛着の対象である security blanket（安心毛布）のようなモノを母親の代理の役目をはたすと考え，transitional object（移行対象／過渡対象）と呼んでいる。

記事の原題は “Our Stuff, Ourselves”（所有物，それは自分自身）。邦題は「愛着の心理学」という一般的なものにしてある。

ないかと推測している。

不安定な愛着スタイルの人が増えるにつれて，形のある物から癒やしを得ようとする行動も増えているようだ。現在は南ミシシッピ大学にいる心理学者のキーファー（Lucas A. Keefer）らが行った興味深い研究によると，人間は大切に思っている人への信頼感が低下すると所有物への執着が増すという。2012 年に *Journal of Experimental Social Psychology* 誌に発表されたこの研究では，まず第 1 グループの被験者に，身近な人に失望した最近の出来事を 3 つ書いてもらった。第 2 グループの被験者には，知らない人に失望した出来事か自分に失望した出来事のどちらかを書いてもらった。他者を頼ることに大きな不安を感じ，物への強い愛着を示したのは，事前に親友や恋人に対する不信感について考えてもらった第 1 グループの被験者だけだった。

この研究の第 3 の部分では，大学生に自分の能力に対する不安か人間関係に対する不安のどちらかを指定し，数行の文章を書いてもらった。その際，被験者全員に自分の携帯電話を提出してもらい，字数制限のない作文を書き終えたらすぐに返却すると伝えた。キーファーによると，人間関係に対する不安について書くよう求められた大学生は携帯電話を手放すことに対する不安（作文課題をどれくらい早く終わらせたかで測定）が強く，急いで取り戻そうとした。社会的ツールとしての携帯電話の有用性に関する被験者の認識を考慮してデータを補正した場合でも，この結果は変わらなかった。

人間は大切な人に失望したとき，なぜ物を求めるのだろう？　着古したトレーナーは人間ではないし，同情もしてくれない。テディベアやマグカップも同様だ。だが，それらは失望させることはないし，常にそこにあって自分の支配下にあると研究者は指摘する。頼りにできるのだ。

Francine Russo
心理学と行動学を専門とするベテランのジャーナリスト。著書に “They’re Your Parents, Too! How Siblings Can Survive Their Parents’ Aging Without Driving Each Other Crazy”（Bantam，2010）がある。

Age of Opportunity

反抗期の脳と
うまく向き合うには

L. デンワース
(SCIENTIFIC AMERICAN編集部)

青年期に起きる脳の成長に関する理解が深まってきた
この知識をうまく使えば，若者に受け入れられる形で有効な助言ができるだろう

KEY CONCEPTS

脳を理解して反抗期に向き合う

■10代は重要な時期だ。ここで悪しき習慣を覚えるとなかなか抜け出せない。だが，“上から目線”のアドバイスは逆効果になりかねない。

■青年期特有の難しさは，この時期の脳の発達の仕方で説明できる。判断や推論などに関わる脳領域がゆっくりと発達するのに対して，感情や報酬，仲間からの期待に反応する領域は急速に発達する。

■思春期は社会的な存在になるための感受期で，脳はそれに応じた成長をする。こうした知見は，相手を尊重したやり方でのアドバイスが若者には有効であることを裏づけている。

日経サイエンス 2021年10月号，SCIENTIFIC AMERICAN May 2021

Here is a parable for our time: There once was an adult who wanted to encourage eighth graders to eat healthier food. The adult designed a lesson plan full of nutritional information—why fruit and vegetables are good for you, why junk food is bad for you, and so on. A similar approach had worked with younger children. But the eighth graders declared the intervention—and, if we're being honest, the adult—boring. They carried on eating junk food, some of them in greater quantities than they had before.

Vocabulary

parable 寓話
our time 現代
eighth grader 8年生(中学2年生)
nutritional 栄養に関する
intervention 口出し
boring うんざり
carry on ～し続ける

Versions of that story play out in real life all the time, although the age of the adolescents varies, and the goal could be anything from reducing bullying or depression to increasing engagement with math. With discouraging regularity, researchers find that what works with younger children is no longer effective with adolescents. Eighth grade seems to be the inflection point.

play out 起こる
adolescent 青少年
bullying いじめ
depression 抑うつ
engagement with ～への取り組み
math 数学
with discouraging regularity がっかりするほど毎度毎度
inflection point 変曲点, 変わり目

If we thought more carefully about what it is to be an eighth grader, however, down to the level of changes in the brain, our parable could have a happier ending. Thirteen-year-olds are concerned with status and respect—these kids do not want to feel patronized by adults. In a study published in 2019 in Nature Human Behaviour, instead of nutritional information, researchers showed more than 300 eighth graders in Texas investigative reports revealing that food company executives use unhealthy ingredients, target young adolescents in their marketing, and won't let their own children eat their products. The students were outraged and began to see healthy eating as a way of taking a stand against being manipulated. For the next three months the students made healthier snack purchases in the cafeteria. And in a follow-up study, the researchers found that the students, especially boys, with higher levels of testosterone (a marker of pubertal maturation in both boys and girls) were most likely to respond well to the intervention.

down to ～に至るまで
patronize "上から目線"で語る
ingredient 原材料
outraged 憤慨した
take a stand against ～に反対の態度をとる
manipulated 思い通りにされる
cafeteria 学校の食堂
follow-up study 追跡研究
testosterone テストステロン
pubertal maturation 思春期の成熟
intervention 介入

Over the past 15 years neuroscience has dramatically changed our understanding of the structural and functional changes in the brain during adolescence, which runs from around the age of 10 all the way into the mid-20s. It is a time of rapid brain growth and neuronal fine-tuning when young people are especially sensitive to social cues and rewards. More recent research has focused on how the adolescent brain interacts with the social environment. It shows that social context and acceptance strongly influence behavior. Adolescence might even constitute a sensitive period for social and emotional learning, a window of time when the brain is uniquely primed by neurochemical changes to make use of social cues for learning.

A growing group of researchers and clinicians see these neuroscientific findings as a chance to do things differently. When a young brain is looking for experience, teachers, parents and other influential adults should seek to capitalize on the richness of learning and stave off negative experiences such as smoking or drug use. This was a central idea in the 2019 National Academies of Sciences, Engineering and Medicine report on the promise of adolescence, which called for investments in programs and interventions that use the brain's capacity to change during adolescence to promote beneficial shifts in young people's life trajectories.

A sensitive period for social and emotional processing also suggests that certain phases of adolescence may be more opportune than others for certain approaches. Early adolescence in particular—from roughly age nine to 11—could be an opportunity to launch kids on a positive path by buttressing their sense of self and motivation to learn. The nutrition experiment shows the benefits of fine-tuning interventions for middle adolescents, who have been through puberty. And no one wants to suggest that it's ever too late to help young people in trouble, especially

Vocabulary

neuroscience 神経科学
adolescence 青年期
neuronal ニューロンの
sensitive 敏感な
social cue 社会的手がかり
reward 見返り
interact 相互作用する
social context 社会的文脈
acceptance 受容, 受け入れられること
sensitive period 感受期
▶この記事の読み方
social and emotional learning 社会的・感情的学習
window of time 期間
prime 下準備する
neurochemical 神経化学的な

clinician 臨床医
capitalize on ～を利用する
stave off 回避する
call for ～を呼びかける, ～を求める
life trajectory 人生の道筋

opportune 好適な
early adolescence 青年期早期
launch 進ませる
positive path 望ましい方向
buttress 強化する
sense of self 自意識
motivation to learn 学習意欲
middle adolescent 青年期中期の若者
puberty 思春期

given that the most serious behavioral and health problems of adolescence tend to occur at 16 and beyond.

To meaningfully compare the results of which interventions work best at age 10 or 14 or 18 requires extensive longitudinal studies, which have not yet been done. Even so, the advances in developmental science appear poised to lead to wiser, more effective approaches to supporting young people's education and physical and mental health. These new methods emphasize adolescents' concern with status and respect, their evolving sense of self in relation to the wider world, and their need to contribute and find purpose. Similar ideas already underpin the growing interest in social and emotional learning among educators. Rather than focusing on the storminess of the teenage years, these ideas offer a sunnier view of adolescence as a window of opportunity.

Rethinking Adolescence

For decades much of the research on adolescence focused on its dark side. Although those years are the physically healthiest period in life, when strength, speed, reaction time, reasoning abilities and immune function all improve or peak, adolescence also brings alarming increases in rates of accidents, suicide, homicide, depression, alcohol and substance use, violence, reckless behaviors, eating disorders, obesity and sexually transmitted disease compared with the rates for younger children.

But a different interpretation of adolescence emerged in the 2000s, stemming from two important new findings. Neuroscientists showed that puberty ushers in a period of exuberant neuronal growth followed by a pruning of neural connections that is second only to the similar process that occurs in the first three years of life. They also showed that the maturation of the adolescent brain is not linear. The limbic system, a collection of brain areas that are sensitive to emotion, reward, novelty, threat and peer

Vocabulary

given that 〜を考えれば

longitudinal study 縦断研究
developmental science 発達科学
evolving 発達する
underpin 支える
storminess 嵐のような荒々しさ
sunnier より明るい, 前向きな
window of opportunity 絶好のチャンス

for decades ここ数十年
reasoning abilities 推論能力
immune function 免疫機能
alarming 驚くべき
homicide 殺人
depression うつ病
substance use 薬物使用
reckless behavior 向こう見ずな行動
eating disorder 摂食障害
obesity 肥満
sexually transmitted disease 性感染症

stem from 〜に由来する
usher in 〜の到来を告げる
exuberant 盛んな
pruning 刈り込み
neural connection 神経接続
linear 直線的な, 一本調子の
limbic system 大脳辺縁系
novelty 新奇性
threat 脅威
peer expectation 仲間の期待

expectations, undergoes a growth spurt while the brain areas responsible for reasoning, judgment and executive function continue their slow, steady march toward adulthood. The resulting imbalance in the developmental forces helps to explain adolescent impulsivity, risk taking, and sensitivity to social reward and learning. From an evolutionary sense, much of adolescents' behavior pushes them to leave the safety of family to explore the larger social world—a step on the way to becoming independent adults.

Vocabulary

executive function 実行機能
imbalance アンバランス
developmental forces 発達の勢い
impulsivity 衝動性, 衝動的行動
risk taking 危険な行動
from an evolutionary sense 進化論的には

Another line of research, from the human connectome project, shows that adult brains vary in their patterns of neural connections throughout the brain, whereas children's connectomes are less distinctive. Those differentiated patterns of connection emerge in adolescence—between the ages of 10 and 16, just when social values and cognition are developing quickly. And the changes in the connectome data show up on average a year to a year and a half earlier in girls than in boys, just like puberty does, which suggests that the two things are intertwined.

human connectome project 「ヒトコネクトーム計画」
less distinctive 個人差が比較的少ない
differentiated patterns 個人差のあるパターン
social values 社会的価値観
cognition 認知
intertwined 関連がある

The idea that adolescence might constitute a sensitive period for social and emotional processing was put forward in 2014 by neuroscientists Sarah-Jayne Blakemore and Kathryn Mills, now at the University of Cambridge and the University of Oregon, respectively. Previous research had assumed that social-cognitive abilities such as theory of mind were mature by the middle of childhood, but Blakemore and Mills laid out the many continuing changes across adolescence in social cognition and the network of brain regions governing social behavior.

put forward 提案された
social-cognitive ability 社会的認知力
theory of mind 「心の理論」
childhood 小児期
lay out 明らかにする
social cognition 社会的認知
brain region 脳領域
govern つかさどる

Sensitive, or critical, periods are windows of time when the brain is primed to make specific neural connections that depend on the input received. They are timed to when important information is available and most useful for development. For sensory processing such as vision and hearing, such periods are well defined with an opening,

critical period 臨界期
specific 特異的な
timed 時期が合致する
sensory processing 感覚処理
vision 視覚
hearing 聴覚
well defined 非常にはっきりしている

peak and closing. A brain deprived of sight or sound early in development will never be able to see or hear normally. Likewise, a sensitive period for language acquisition explains why people who learn a foreign language after puberty typically have an accent. Sensitive periods for social learning have been harder to pin down.

Animal research has identified some versions of sensitive periods for social learning. Songbirds can delay the closing of the sensitive period for vocal learning if they need more time to learn their songs, which usually happens in adolescence. "It's a gorgeous example of a sensitive period for learning that has social function," says Linda Wilbrecht of the University of California, Berkeley, who has studied sensitive periods in songbirds, mice and humans.

Neuroscientist Gül Dölen and her colleagues at Johns Hopkins University identified an adolescent critical period in mice for something called social conditioned place preference (social CPP). The research followed up on an observation by the late Estonian neuroscientist Jaak Panksepp. He presented mice with two different kinds of bedding—on one, the mice were alone; on the other, they were with friends. When the mice subsequently had a choice of bedding, adolescents, in particular, showed a preference for the bedding that carried a memory of friends.

Dölen ran similar experiments with roughly 900 mice at 14 different ages and mapped out exactly when this preference for place occurs. Triggered by changes in oxytocin that lead to increased synaptic plasticity, it peaks 42 days after birth (roughly age 14 in humans), when the mice become sexually mature. "It's a really important stage of their lives when they're leaving the nest and trying to create their own groups," Dölen says. "[In] that window of time, when they're really sensitive to what other members

Vocabulary

opening 始まり
closing 終わり
deprived of ～を奪われた
language acquisition 言語習得
accent なまり
social learning 社会的学習
pin down 特定する

songbird 鳴禽類
vocal learning 音声学習
gorgeous 素晴らしい

social conditioned place preference 社会的条件づけ場所嗜好性
follow up on ～をさらに深める
bedding 寝床
in particular 特に

map out 明らかにする
trigger 誘発する
oxytocin オキシトシン
synaptic plasticity シナプスの可塑性
▶この記事の読み方

of their group are doing, when they're learning from their group, when they're forming attachments to the group—that's when that peaks." It seems the brain is suddenly alert to and rewarded by information that it had previously ignored. "There's information flowing by us all the time," Wilbrecht says. "Once puberty and hormones pass through the circuit, suddenly those cues have meaning. They don't have salience until you shift into the adolescent phase."

Vocabulary

attachment 愛着
alert to ～に注意を向ける
salience 目立った重要性

現代の寓話を1つ紹介しよう。ある人が，中学2年生にもっと健康的なものを食べてもらいたいと思った。そこで，どうして果物と野菜は体に良いのか，どうしてジャンクフードは体に悪いのかといった栄養学的な知識を盛り込んだ授業を計画した。このやり方は，もっと低学年の子どもではうまくいった。だが，中学2年生は，「そんな口出しをされるのも口出しする大人にもうんざりだ」と言い放った。彼らはジャンクフードを食べ続け，前よりたくさん食べるようになった子さえいた。

同じようなことは実生活でもしょっちゅう起きている。助言に耳を貸さない青少年の年齢はさまざまだが，いじめや抑うつを減らすことから数学の勉強を奨励することまで，多くのアドバイスが決まって反発を買う。年少の子どもではうまくいく方法も若者では効果がないらしい。中学2年はその変わり目のようだ。

中学2年生とはどういうものかを脳の変化のレベルでより深く考えれば，この寓話をハッピーエンドの物語に変えられる可能性がある。13歳の子どもは集団の中での地位や自分が尊重されているかどうかを気にかけ，“上から目線”で語る大人に反発する。2019年に *Nature Human Behaviour* 誌に発表された研究は，まったく別のアプローチを試していた。テキサス州の300人以上の中学2年生に対して栄養学的な知識ではなく，食品会社の経営陣は健康に良くない原材料を使って若者向けの製品を作っており，我が子には自社製品を食べさせようとしないという調査報告書を紹介したのだ。生徒たちは憤慨し，健康的な食事をすることを食品会社の思い通りにはならないことを示す方法とみなすようになった。生徒たちが学校の食堂で買った軽食をその後の3カ月にわたって調べたところ，健康により良いものを選んでいた。さらにその後の研究では，テストステロン濃度（男子と女子の両方で思春期の成熟を示すマーカーの1つ）が高い生徒，特に男子はこの介入に顕著に反応する傾向が見られた。

過去15年間の神経科学的な研究によって，青年期（10歳ころから20代半ばまで）における脳の構造的・機能的な変化についての理解は劇的に変わった。この時期の脳は急速に成長するだけでなく神経系の微調整が行われ，若者は社会的手がかり（相手の表情や身振りなど，自分の行動のきっかけとなる手がかり）や見返りに対して特に敏感に反応するようになる。より最近の研究は，青年期の脳が社会的環境にどのように反応するかに注目してきた。それにより，社会的文脈と周囲に受け入れられるかどうかが行動に強く影響することがわかった。青年期は，社会的・感情的学習の「感受期」，すなわち，脳の神経化学的な変化により，社会的手がかりを学びに生かすことが可能な期間であると言ってよいだろう。

こうした神経科学的な発見を，若者との接し方を変えるためのチャンスとみなす研究者や医師が増えている。若い脳が経験を積もうとしているとき，彼らに大きな影響を及ぼすことができる教師や親などの大人は，この豊かな学習力を利用して喫煙や薬物使用といった悪習慣から彼らを遠ざけるようにすべきだ。この考え方は，全米アカデミーズが 2019 年に発表した青年期の可能性に関する

この記事の読み方

原題は "Age of Opportunity"（好機の年齢）。社会的・感情的学習の感受期について述べた記事である。社会性に関与する脳領域では，もっぱら青年期に神経回路網の形成が起こることを示す研究が紹介されている。

ここで感受期のほかの例として挙げられているのは，人間での言語習得と鳴禽類の歌の学習。どちらも，思春期や性的成熟期の終わりが感受期の終わりに相当する。感受期には，脳内では oxytocin（オキシトシン）が synaptic plasticity（シナプスの可塑性）に影響を与えていることを示すマウスでの実験も紹介されている。

sensitive period をここでは「感受期」と訳してあるが，「敏感期」と訳すことも可能である（どちらを採るかは分野や好みによる）。類語に critical period（臨界期）があるが，こちらは期間がクリアカットに決まっている場合に用いられる。ただ，本記事中でも「感受期（あるいは臨界期）」と書いているように，互換性のある使われ方をすることが多い。

記事の後半では，これらの知見を青年期の社会的学習に生かすにはどうすればよいか（若者への接し方，アドバイスの仕方など）が示唆されている。邦題にはこの内容が反映されている。

報告書の核心部分となっている。この報告書では，青年期に起きる脳の変化を利用し，若者の人生の道筋に有益な変化を促すようなプログラムと介入活動に投資するよう呼びかけている。

社会的・感情的処理の感受期だということは，青年期には特定のアプローチがとりわけうまくいく時期がある可能性も示唆している。特に 9 〜 11 歳頃の青年期早期は，自意識と学習意欲を高めることによって子どもを望ましい方向に進ませる良い機会となりうるだろう。前述の栄養をテーマにした実験では，思春期を経た青年期中期の若者に対して，助言の仕方を少し変えることで大きなプラス効果が生じた。青年期の最も深刻な健康上・行動上の問題が 16 歳以降に生じる傾向があることを考えればなおのこと，問題を抱えた若者をすでに手遅れとみなして見捨てるようなことは誰も望んではいない。

10 歳，14 歳，18 歳の若者に対してどのようなアプローチが最も有効かをきちんと比較するには，長期にわたる縦断研究が必要だが，まだ実施されたことはない。それでも発達科学の進歩によって，若者の教育と心身の健康を支えるより効果の高い方法が見つかりそうだ。これらの新たな方法で強調されているのは，若者が集団での地位や自分が尊重されているかどうかに強い関心をもつこと，もっと広い世界との関わりによって自意識が発達すること，社会に貢献し，目的を見つけることを必要としていることなどである。同様の考え方に基づき，すでに教育者の間では社会的・感情的な学習に対する関心が高まっている。青年期を 10 代の嵐のような時期としてではなく，絶好のチャンスとしてとらえるずっと前向きな考え方だ。

独特の成長をする青年期の脳

ここ数十年，青年期の研究はマイナスの側面に注目したものがほとんどだった。青年期は人生において身体的に最も健康的で，体力やスピード，反応時間，推論能力，免疫機能のどれもが上向きかピークにある時期だが，一方で，事故や自殺，殺人，うつ病，アルコールや薬物の使用，暴力，向こう見ずな行動，摂食障害，肥満，性感染症の比率は，下の年齢の子どもと比べて急増する。

だが，2000年代になると，2つの新たな重要な知見から青年期に対する別の見方が出てきた。生後の3年間で，ニューロンの盛んな増殖と神経接続の“刈り込み”というプロセスが起きるが，思春期にも同様の変化がもう一度起こることが神経科学者によって示されたのだ。また，青年期の脳の成熟は，それぞれの領域が足並みをそろえて一本調子に進むものではないこともわかった。感情や報酬，新奇性，脅威，仲間の期待などに敏感に反応する領域の集まった大脳辺縁系が急激に成長する一方で，推論や判断，実行機能に関わる脳領域は成人期までゆっくり地道に成長し続ける。この結果として生じる脳の発達のアンバランスは，青年たちの衝動的な行動や危険な行動，社会的報酬と社会的学習に敏感であることの説明になる。進化論的には，若者の行動の多くは親に守られた安全な場を離れてもっと大きな社会の探検を促すものであり，自立した大人になるための1つの段階だ。

また，ヒトの神経回路をすべてマッピングすることを目指す「ヒトコネクトーム計画」の研究から，成人の脳は人によって神経接続のパターンがあちこちで異なっているのに対し，子どもではそうした個人差が比較的少ないことがわかった。こうした神経接続のパターンに個人差が生じる10～16歳の青年期は，ちょうど社会的価値観と社会的認知が急速に発達する時期に当たる。また思春期の訪れと同じように，コネクトームのデータに変化が表れるのは女子の方が男子より1年から1年半早い。これは，思春期とコネクトームの変化に関連があることを示唆している。

青年期が社会的・感情的処理の感受期になっているという考え方は，現在は英ケンブリッジ大学にいる神経科学者ブレイクモア（Sarah-Jayne Blakemore）とオレゴン大学のミルズ（Kathryn Mills）が2014年に提案したものだ。それまでの研究では，「心の理論」といった社会的認知力は小児期中期までに成熟すると考えられていた。だが，ブレイクモアとミルズは，青年期には社会的行動をつかさどる脳領域のネットワークと社会的認知に多くの変化が起き続けていることを明らかにした。

感受期（あるいは臨界期）とは，脳が受け取った入力に基づいて特異的な神経接続を形成できる期間のことだ。感受期は，重要な情報が入力され，その情報が発達上で最も役立つような時期と合致している。視覚や聴覚のような感覚処理の感受期は，始まり・ピーク・終わりが非常にはっきりしている。発達の初期に視覚情報や聴覚情報を得られなかった脳は，正常に見聞きできるようにならない。同様に，言語習得にも感受期があるとされ，思春期以降に外国語を習った人はなまりが生じやすいことの裏づけとなっている。一方，社会的学習の感受期はなかなか特定しにくい。

動物の研究では，社会的学習に関する感受期が特定されているものもある。例えばウグイスやヒタキなどの小型でよくさえずる鳴禽類（めいきんるい）は通常は幼いうちに“歌”を学習するが，学習にもっと時間が必要なときには音声学習の感受期の終了を青年期まで遅らせることができる。カリフォルニア大学バークレー校で鳴禽類とマウス，ヒトの感受期について研究しているウィルブレヒト（Linda Wilbrecht）は，「これは学習の感受期が社会的機能を担っていることを示す素晴らしい一例だ」と言う。

ジョンズ・ホプキンズ大学の神経科学者のドーレン（Gül Dölen）らは，青年期のマウスで「社会的条件づけ場所嗜好性（社会的 CPP）」と呼ばれるものの感受期を確認した。この研究は，エストニアの神経科学者である故パンクセップ（Jaak Panksepp）の観察結果を深めたものだ。パンクセップはマウスに自分だけがいた寝床と，仲間と一緒にいた寝床の 2 つを示して，どちらかをマウスに選ばせる実験をした。青年期のマウスは特に，仲間といた寝床を選んだ。

ドーレンは約 900 匹のマウスの日齢を 14 段階に分けて同様の実験を行い，この場所嗜好性が正確にいつ始まるのかを明らかにした。場所嗜好性は，シナプス（神経細胞の接続部位）の可塑性を増加させるホルモンであるオキシトシンの濃度変化によって誘導され，マウスが性成熟する生後 42 日目（ヒトでは 14 歳頃に相当）でピークに達した。「これはマウスの一生にとって非常に重要な段階であり，彼らはこの時期に巣を離れて自分の群れを作ろうとする」とドーレンは言う。「この期間は群れの仲間がしていることに非常に敏感に反応し，群れから学習し，群れに対する愛着を形成する時期で，場所嗜好性もピークになる」。脳は，それまで無視していた情報に突然注意を向け，その情報から報酬を得るようになったように見える。「情報は常に私たちの周囲にあふれているが」とウィルブレヒトは言う。「思春期になってホルモンが脳の回路に流れると，それらの社会的手がかりが突然意味をもつようになる。青年期に入るまではほとんど注意を引かなかったのに」。

Lydia Denworth
米ニューヨーク州ブルックリンを拠点とするサイエンスライターで，SCIENTIFIC AMERICAN 誌の寄稿編集者。著書に“Friendship：The Evolution, Biology, and Extraordinary Power of Life’s Fundamental Bond”（W.W.Norton，2020）がある。

Baby Talk

赤ちゃんの超言語力

P. K. クール
（米ワシントン大学）

子どもはみな生まれながらにして
世界に7000ある言語のいずれをも習得する能力を持っている

KEY CONCEPTS

生来の能力と社会的相互作用で学習

■赤ちゃんの脳は生後6カ月で「敏感期」に入る。母国語や他言語の音を最もよく認識できるようになるこの時期は，ネイティブスピーカーが話す流暢な口調やイントネーションを身につけるための準備期間となる。

■生来の言語能力は，それだけでパパやママといった最初の発語を引き出せるわけではない。言語というこの非常に重要な社会的スキルを身につけるには，赤ちゃんが両親の話しかけに長期間注意を払う必要がある。

■初期の言語学習に関する知見が十分集まってきたので，脳活動を計測して子どもの脳が正常な発達をたどっているかどうかを検査できる可能性が出てきた。

日経サイエンス 2016年3月号，SCIENTIFIC AMERICAN November 2015

In infant child possesses an amazing, and fleeting, gift: the ability to master a language quickly. At six months, the child can learn the sounds that make up English words and, if also exposed to Quechua and Tagalog, he or she can pick up the unique acoustic properties of those languages, too. By age three, a toddler can converse with a parent, a playmate or a stranger.

I still marvel, after four decades of studying child development, how a child can go from random babbling to speaking fully articulated words and sentences just a few years later—a mastery that occurs more quickly than any complex skill acquired during the course of a lifetime. Only in the past few years have neuroscientists begun to get a picture of what is happening in a baby's brain during this learning process that takes the child from gurgling newborn to a wonderfully engaging youngster.

At birth, the infant brain can perceive the full set of 800 or so sounds, called phonemes, that can be strung together to form all the words in every language of the world. During the second half of the first year, our research shows, a mysterious door opens in the child's brain. He or she enters a "sensitive period," as neuroscientists call it, during which the infant brain is ready to receive the first basic lessons in the magic of language.

The time when a youngster's brain is most open to learning the sounds of a native tongue begins at six months for vowels and at nine months for consonants. It appears that the sensitive period lasts for only a few months but is extended for children exposed to sounds of a second language. A child can still pick up a second language with a fair degree of fluency until age seven.

The built-in capacity for language is not by itself enough to get a baby past the first utterances of "Mama" and "Dada." Gaining mastery of the most import-

Vocabulary

[タイトル] **baby talk** 赤ちゃん言葉
▶この記事の読み方

infant child 幼児, 子ども
▶この記事の読み方
fleeting 束の間の
gift 天賦の才能
make up 構成する
expose 触れさせる, 聞かせる
Quechua ケチュア語
Tagalog タガログ語
pick up 習得する, 覚える
acoustic property 音響特性
toddler よちよち歩きの幼児
converse 会話をする

marvel 驚く
babbling 喃語
articulated はっきりと発音された
mastery 熟達
neuroscientist 神経科学者
get a picture of ～の輪郭をつかむ
gurgling 喉をゴロゴロ鳴らす
newborn 新生児
engaging 愛嬌のある
youngster 子ども, 若者

perceive 知覚する, 認識する
phoneme 音素
string together つなぎ合わせる
sensitive period 敏感期, 感受期

native tongue 母語, 母国語
▶この記事の読み方
vowel 母音
consonant 子音
second language 第2言語
with a fair degree of fluency かなり流暢に

built-in 生来の
by itself それ自体では, それだけでは

ant of all social skills is helped along by countless hours listening to parents speak the silly vernacular of "parentese." Its exaggerated inflections—"You're a preettee babbee"—serve the unfrivolous purpose of furnishing daily lessons in the intonations and cadences of the baby's native tongue. Our work puts to rest the age-old debates about whether genes or the environment prevails during early language development. They both play starring roles.

Knowledge of early language development has now reached a level of sophistication that is enabling psychologists and physicians to fashion new tools to help children with learning difficulties. Studies have begun to lay the groundwork for using recordings of brain waves to determine whether a child's language abilities are developing normally or whether an infant may be at risk for autism, attention deficit or other disorders. One day a routine visit to the pediatrician may involve a baby brain examination, along with vaccinations for measles, mumps and rubella.

The Statistics of Baby Talk

The reason we can contemplate a test for language development is that we have begun to understand how babies absorb language with seeming ease. My laboratory and others have shown that infants use two distinct learning mechanisms at the earliest stages of language acquisition: one that recognizes sound through mental computation and another that requires intense social immersion.

To learn to speak, infants have to know which phonemes make up the words they hear all around them. They need to discriminate which 40 or so, out of all 800, phonemes they need to learn to speak words in their own language. This task requires detecting subtle differences in spoken sound. A change in a single consonant can alter the meaning of a word—"bat" to "pat," for instance. And a simple vowel like "ah" varies widely when spoken by different people at different speaking rates and in different con-

Vocabulary

get someone past ～を通過させる
utterance 発声，発話
social skill 社会的スキル
vernacular 特有の言葉(づかい)
parentese ペアレンティーズ，親語
▶この記事の読み方
exaggerated 大げさな
inflection 抑揚
unfrivolous 重要な，ちゃんとした
furnish 提供する，授ける
cadence リズム
put to rest 決着をもたらす
gene 遺伝子
prevail 優位を占める
starring role 主役，中心的役割

fashion 作り出す
learning difficulty 学習障害
lay the groundwork 基礎を敷く
autism 自閉症
attention deficit 注意欠陥
pediatrician 小児科医
vaccination ワクチン接種
measles はしか，麻疹
mumps おたふく風邪
rubella 風疹

statistics 統計学
contemplate ～について考える
absorb 身につける
with seeming ease 一見やすやすと
distinct 異なる
language acquisition 言語習得
mental computation 脳での統計処理
intense social immersion 他者と社会的に密接に関係すること

discriminate 識別する
subtle 微妙な
speaking rate 話す速さ
context 文脈

texts—"Bach" versus "rock." Extreme variation in phonemes is why Apple's Siri still does not work flawlessly.

My work and that of Jessica Maye, then at Northwestern University, and her colleagues have shown that statistical patterns—the frequency with which sounds occur—play a critical role in helping infants learn which phonemes are most important. Children between eight and 10 months of age still do not understand spoken words. Yet they are highly sensitive to how often phonemes occur—what statisticians call distributional frequencies. The most important phonemes in a given language are the ones spoken most. In English, for example, the "r" and "l" sounds are quite frequent. They appear in words such as "rake" and "read" and "lake" and "lead." In Japan, the English-like "r" and "l" also occur but not as often. Instead the Japanese "r" sound is common but is rarely found in English. (The Japanese word "raamen" sounds like "laamen" to American ears because the Japanese "r" is midway between the American "r" and "l.")

The statistical frequency of particular sounds affects the infant brain. In one study of infants in Seattle and Stockholm, we monitored their perception of vowel sounds at six months and demonstrated that each group had already begun to focus in on the vowels spoken in their native language. The culture of the spoken word had already pervaded and affected how the baby's brain perceived sounds.

What exactly was going on here? Maye has shown that the brain at this age has the requisite plasticity to change how infants perceive sounds. A Japanese baby who hears sounds from English learns to distinguish the "r" and the "l" in the way they are used in the U.S. And a baby being raised among native English speakers could likewise pick up the characteristic sounds of Japanese. It appears that learning sounds in the second half of the first year

Vocabulary

flawlessly そつなく, 完璧に

frequency 頻度
critical きわめて重要な, 決定的な
statistician 統計学者
distributional frequency 度数分布
frequent 頻出する

perception 知覚, 認識
demonstrate 明らかにする
native language 母語, 母国語
pervade 浸透する

going on 起きている
requisite 必須の
plasticity 可塑性, 柔軟性
characteristic 特有の

establishes connections in the brain for one's native tongue but not for other languages, unless a child is exposed to multiple languages during that period.

Later in childhood, and particularly as an adult, listening to a new language does not produce such dramatic results—a traveler to France or Japan can hear the statistical distributions of sounds from another language, but the brain is not altered by the experience. That is why it is so difficult to pick up a second language later on.

A second form of statistical learning lets infants recognize whole words. As adults, we can distinguish where one word ends and the next begins. But the ability to isolate words from the stream of speech requires complex mental processing. Spoken speech arrives at the ear as a continuous stream of sound that lacks the separations found between written words.

Jenny Saffran, now at the University of Wisconsin–Madison, and her colleagues—Richard Aslin of the University of Rochester and Elissa Newport, now at Georgetown University—were the first to discover that a baby uses statistical learning to grasp the sounds of whole words. In the mid-1990s Saffran's group published evidence that eight-month-old infants can learn wordlike units based on the probability that one syllable follows another. Take the phrase "pretty baby." The syllable "pre" is more likely to be heard with "ty" than to accompany another syllable like "ba."

In the experiment, Saffran had babies listen to streams of computer-synthesized nonsense words that contained syllables, some of which occurred together more often than others. The babies' ability to focus on syllables that coincide in the made-up language let them identify likely words.

Vocabulary

multiple 複数の

childhood 小児期
alter 変える

statistical learning 統計的学習
▶この記事の読み方
isolate 分離する
complex mental processing 脳での複雑な処理
separation 区切り

grasp 把握する
probability 確率，頻度
syllable 音節
take 例にとる

nonsense 無意味な
coincide 連なって現れる，セットになって聞こえる
made-up でっち上げた，架空の
likely word 単語らしきもの

The discovery of babies' statistical-learning abilities in the 1990s generated a great deal of excitement because it offered a theory of language learning beyond the prevailing idea that a child learns only because of parental conditioning and affirmations of whether a word is right or wrong. Infant learning occurs before parents realize that it is taking place. Further tests in my lab, however, produced a significant new finding that lends an important caveat to this story: the statistical-learning process does not require passive listening alone.

Vocabulary

prevailing 支配的な, 一般的な
conditioning 条件づけ
affirmation 確認, 肯定
take place 起こる
lend 添える, 加える
caveat ただし書き
passive listening 受動的に聞くこと

子どもは言語を急速に習得するという驚くべき（そして束の間の）天賦の才能を持っている。生後 6 カ月で母国語の単語を構成する音を覚え，またケチュア語やタガログ語を聞かせれば，これらの言語特有の音を覚えることもできる。3 歳になれば，親や遊び友達，見知らぬ人とも会話ができる。

私は 40 年にわたって子どもの発達について研究してきたが，めちゃくちゃな喃語（なんご）を発していた乳児がわずか数年で言葉や文をはっきり話せるようになるのにはいまだに驚かされる。子どもは，人生の過程で身につけるどんな複雑なスキルよりも急速に言語を覚える。あーうーと言っていた新生児が驚くほど愛嬌のある子どもになるまでのこの学習の過程では脳で何が起きているのか，その全体像がここ数年でようやく明らかになってきた。

誕生時の赤ちゃんは，世界の言語に 800 種類ほどある「音素」をすべて認識する能力がある。この音素がつながって，あらゆる言語のすべての単語が構成されている。生後 6 カ月から 1 年の間に，子どもの脳で秘密のドアが開くことが私たちの研究から示されている。神経科学でいう「敏感期」に入ると，子どもは言葉という魔法の最初の基礎レッスンを受けられるようになる。

子どもの脳が母国語の音を最も覚えやすくなる時期は，母音については生後 6 カ月，子音については 9 カ月ごろから始まる。敏感期は 2 ～ 3 カ月しか続かないが，第 2 言語の音に触れた場合にはそれが延びるようだ。子どもは 7 歳までであれば第 2 言語を覚えてかなり流暢に話せるようになる。

だが，赤ちゃんの生来の言語能力だけでは「ママ」や「パパ」といった最初の言葉は引き出せない。言語というこの極めて重要なソーシャルスキルの習得は，親が話す奇妙な「ペアレンティーズ（親語）」に非常に長い時間耳を傾けることで成り立つ。“You’re a preetee babbee（かわいい赤ちゃん）” といった大げさな抑揚にはちゃんとした役目があり，赤ちゃんが母国語のイントネーションやリズムを覚えるための日々のレッスンになっている。私たちの研究は，初期の言語発達において遺伝と環境のどちらがより重要なのかという議論に決着をもたらした。どちらも中心的役割を担っているのだ。

初期の言語発達に関する知見が十分に集まってきたので，学習障害のある子どもに役立つ新しい手立てを考えられるようになった。子どもの言語能力が正常に発達しているのか，それとも自閉症や注意欠陥などの障害を持つリスクがあるかどうかを，脳波を計測して調べる基礎研究が始まっている。将来は小児科を定期的に受診する際に，麻疹・風疹・おたふく風邪の予防接種と一緒に赤ちゃんの脳の検査も行うようになるかもしれない。

統計をもとに学習

私たちが言語発達検査について考えられるようになったのは，どのようにして赤ちゃんがすんなりと言葉を身につけるのかがわかってきたからだ。私たちや他のグループの研究で，言語習得の最初期段階で乳児が 2 種類の学習メカニズムを用いていることが明らかになった。脳での統計処理を通じて音を識別す

この記事の読み方

記事の原題は“Baby Talk”。baby talk は，赤ちゃん自身の話し方ではなく，まわりの大人が赤ちゃんに向けて話す話し方を指し,「赤ちゃん言葉」や「幼児語」と訳される。parentese（ペアレンティーズ／親語）や motherese（マザリーズ／母親語）もこれとほぼ同義で用いられる。

記事では,赤ちゃんが言語音に対して statistical learning（統計的学習）を行っていることを紹介したうえで（掲載文はここまで），親語が赤ちゃんの言語発達にどのような効果を持つのかが議論されている。

native tongue は厳密には「母語」と訳すべきだが,記事中には motherese（母親語）も出てくるので，混同を避けるため「母国語」で訳してある。sensitive period は，前の記事では「感受期」で訳したが，この記事では「敏感期」で訳してある。

infant は日本語では必ずしも一語に対応しない。可能ならば，言及されている子の月齢や年齢，そして文脈に応じて，赤ちゃん，新生児，乳児，幼児，乳幼児，子どもというように訳し分けたほうが丁寧な訳文になる。ちなみに,語源的には,infant は「話すことができない」という意味のラテン語に由来する。

る方法と，他者と社会的に密接な関係を結ぶことによる方法だ。

乳児が話すことを覚えるには，周囲から聞こえる単語がどのような音素で構成されているかを知らなければならない。母国語を話せるようになるには，全部で 800 ある音素のうち母国語が用いる約 40 種類を識別する必要がある。そのためには微妙な発音の違いを聞き取らなくてはならない。単語の意味は，例えば bat（コウモリ）と pat（軽くたたく）のように，子音の違い 1 つで変わってしまう。また，ア（ɑ́）のような単純な母音も話す人や速さによって大きく異なるし，Bach（bɑ́:k, バッハ）と rock（rɑ́k, 岩）のようにまるで違う文脈に登場する。アップルの音声認識ソフト Siri がいまだ完璧には機能しないのは，音素の幅が大きいからだ。

私の研究と当時ノースウェスタン大学にいたメイ（Jessica Maye）の研究では，乳児がどの音素が最も重要かを学ぶ際に，音の頻度という統計パターンが決定的役割を果たしていることを示した。8 カ月齢から 10 カ月齢の乳児は話し言葉をまだ理解していない。しかし，音素がどれくらいの頻度で聞こえるか（統計学でいう度数分布）については非常に敏感だ。ある言語において最も重要な音素とは，最も頻繁に出現する音素だ。例えば英語では r と l の音が非常に多く，rake（熊手）や read（読む），lake（湖）や lead（先導する）といった単語に出てくる。一方，日本語で r と l に相当する音は，一般的ではあるが英語ほど頻度は高くない〔日本語のこの音は英語の r と l の中間の音なので，日本語のラーメン（raamen）の発音は，米国人には laamen のように聞こえる〕。

特定の音が聞こえるこの頻度が，乳児の脳に影響を及ぼす。私たちはシアトルとストックホルムに住む 6 カ月齢の乳児の母音の認識を調べ，どちらの乳児もすでに自分の母国語に含まれる母音に注目し始めていることを明らかにした。耳にした言語文化がすでに乳児の脳に浸透し，音の認識に影響を及ぼしていたのだ。

赤ちゃんの脳ではいったい何が起きているのか？　メイは，この月齢の脳は柔軟性が非常に高く，音の認識の仕方を変えられることを示した。日本人の赤ちゃんは英語の音を聞くと，米国で使われている r と l の音を区別できるようになる。同様に英語のネイティブスピーカーに囲まれて育った赤ちゃんも，日本語特有の音を認識できるようになる。生後半年から 1 年で学んだ音によって，脳では母国語の神経系の接続が確立し，その時期に複数の言語に接していない限りは別の言語の接続は確立しないようだ。

小児期後期以降，特に大人になってからは，新しい言語を聞いても劇的な影響は生じない。外国旅行をすれば外国語の音素の頻度の違いを耳にすることはできるが，その経験で脳は変わらない。成長してから第 2 言語を習得するのが難しいのはこのためだ。

次の統計的学習は，単語そのものの認識だ。大人は 1 つの単語がどこで終わり，どこから次が始まるかがわかる。だが，会話の流れから単語を分離するには，脳での複雑な処理を要する。話し言葉は連続した音の流れとして聞こえ，書かれた言葉とは違って句読点や単語を分離するスペースはない。

現在はウィスコンシン大学マディソン校にいるサフラン（Jenny Saffran）とロチェスター大学のアスリン（Richard Aslin），現在はジョージタウン大学にいるニューポート（Elissa Newport）は，赤ちゃんがひとまとまりの音を単語としてとらえるのに統計的学習を使っていることを最初に見いだした。1990 年代半ば，サフランらは 8 カ月齢の乳児がある音節に続く音節の頻度をもとに単語らしきまとまりを識別していることを示し，発表した。pretty baby（かわいい赤ちゃん）という語句を例にとると，pre という音節の後に ty を伴うことの方が，ba のような他の音節を伴うことよりも多い。

サフランらは実験で，コンピューターで合成した一連の無意味な“単語”を乳児に聞かせた。これらの“単語”は，一部の音節がセットになって続く確率が他の組み合わせよりも高くなるようにしてあった。この架空の言語を聞いた乳児は，セットになって聞こえる音節に注目することで単語らしきものを特定した。

赤ちゃんの統計的学習能力に関する 1990 年代の発見は大きな反響を呼んだ。両親が条件づけをしたり単語の正否を教えてやることによってのみ乳幼児が言葉を学習するというそれまでの考えを超えた言語学習理論が示されたからだ。乳幼児の学習は親がそれに気づく前に始まっている。だが私たちのさらなる研究で重要な新発見があり，これに重要なただし書きが付け加えられた。この統計的な学習は，ただ受動的に聞くだけでは十分に進まないのだ。

Patricia K. Kuhl
米ワシントン大学（シアトル）でベゾス家族財団幼児学習寄付講座の教授ならびに学習・脳科学研究所の共同所長を務めている。全米科学財団（NSF）が資金提供する学習科学センターであるLIFEセンターの所長も務める。

脳と心

3

The Path to Better Childhoods

子育て支援の神経科学

When Pretending Is the Remedy

プラセボ効果の脳科学

Making AI More Human

子どもの脳に学ぶ AI

How Matter Becomes Mind

神経回路網はどのように知性を生み出すのか

The Path to Better Childhoods

子育て支援の神経科学

D. サスキンド
（米シカゴ大学）

L. デンワース
（SCIENTIFIC AMERICAN 編集部）

脳の発達に関する最新の科学的知見からすれば
子どもの学習能力向上や明るい将来のために国がやるべきことは明確だ

KEY CONCEPTS

育児支援が子どもの脳の発達を左右する

■近年の神経科学の成果は，乳幼児の適切な育児環境が，実際に彼らの脳の神経活動を活発にし，脳の発達に寄与することを示している。

■言語の発達には子ども自身の会話への参加が重要なことや，親による有給の産後休業の取得が子どもの発達に良い効果を持つことがわかってきた。

■科学が示す子どもに必要な支援と米国が実施している育児支援には壊滅的なギャップがあり，科学的根拠に基づいて速やかに改善する必要がある。

日経サイエンス 2023 年 3 月号，SCIENTIFIC AMERICAN June 2022

On vital measures that predict later success in school and life, small children in the U.S. do worse than kids in comparable countries. This distressing information comes from an Organisation for Economic Cooperation and Development (OECD) study of five-year-olds. For years the OECD has been examining the academic achievement of 15-year-old students from around the world, and recently it extended this work to the younger group. On average, American children had lower literacy and numeracy scores, poorer self-regulation skills, and engaged in fewer acts of cooperation, kindness and other prosocial behaviors than did children in England and Estonia, the other countries studied. Just about the only bright spot was that U.S. children were roughly equivalent to their international peers on some—but not all—social-emotional measures.

These findings did not get the attention they deserved, because they were announced in March 2020, a few days after the World Health Organization declared that COVID had become a pandemic. But they did not come as a surprise—other recent research has shown that about half of American children are not "on track" in at least one critical area of school readiness. Because the OECD report looked at kids who were just starting school, it was a powerful reminder that we have lost sight of something basic: Learning begins on the first day of life—and not the first day of class. The earliest years of a child's life are full of opportunity. A child's brain will never be more receptive to experience, more plastic, than it is during this pivotal time. Nearly 85 percent of brain growth occurs between birth and the age of three. During this period one million neural connections per second are formed.

Two decades of child development research tell us that small kids need two things above all else to get off to the best possible start: nurturing interaction with caregivers and protection from toxic stress. Over the past five years a new wave of neuroscientific studies, highlighting the neu-

Vocabulary

［タイトル］**childhoods** 幼年期, 子ども時代

vital measures 重要な尺度
distressing 悩ましい
for years 長年
academic achievement 学習到達度
literacy 読み書き
numeracy 計算能力
self-regulation skill 自己調整能力
prosocial 向社会的な
bright spot 明るい材料
equivalent 同等な
peer （年齢などが）同等の者
social-emotional 社会情動的な

deserve 受けるに値する, しかるべき
on track 軌道に乗って
critical 重要な
school readiness 就学準備
reminder 思い出させるもの
lose sight of ～を見失う
receptive 受け入れやすい
plastic 可塑性がある
pivotal きわめて重要な
neural connection 神経接続

development 発達
get off to ~ start ～なスタートを切る
nurturing interaction with caregivers 養育者との親密な関わり
toxic 有害な

robiological effects of early experience, has strongly pointed toward ways of accomplishing these goals. Such research provides an early peek at what is happening in young children's brains. The studies show that environments and relationships we know benefit development are also associated with higher levels of activation and connectivity in parts of the brain that underpin language and cognitive development.

One of us (Suskind) is a pediatric physician and early-learning researcher who has been tracking the way emerging science on brain development can inform not just what we do as parents but as a society. For instance, paid leave gives parents time to develop nurturing relationships. Child allowances and tax credits can alleviate the poverty known to be detrimental to development. When parents work outside the home, as a considerable majority of American mothers and fathers must, access to quality child care provides young children with responsive, engaged caregivers.

Yet there is a disconnect between what science tells us children need and what we as a society do to help them. The U.S. is the only developed country in the world that does not mandate paid leave for a parent after childbirth. In 2020 four in 10 children in the U.S. had families who were struggling to afford basic necessities.

The science of brain development is rarely part of any public discussion of ways to fix these gaps. But it should be at the center of that conversation because it lays out a road map to improve national and local policies that can make children's lives much better.

Vocabulary

neurobiological 神経生物学的な
activation 賦活, 活性化
connectivity 接続
underpin 支える, 担う
cognitive development 認知発達

pediatric physician 小児科医
early learning 早期学習, 幼児教育
emerging science 最新の科学的知見
paid leave 有給休暇
nurturing 子育ての, 養育の
child allowance 児童手当
tax credit 税額控除
alleviate 軽減する
poverty 貧困
detrimental 有害な, 悪影響を及ぼす
child care 保育
engaged 熱心な
caregiver 保育士

disconnect ずれ, 隔たり
mandate 義務付ける
basic necessities 生活必需品
lapse 失効する
weather 乗り切る, 乗り越える
further さらに
child care desert "保育砂漠"地域
highlight 浮き彫りにする
lingering 延々と続く
aftershock 余震
shaky 弱体な, 不安定な

rarely めったにない

The Many Effects of Language

Wearing his ever present Chicago Bulls cap, Randy settled onto the soft carpet of his living room and pulled his two-year-old son, Julian, into his lap.

"Want to play?" he asked.

Julian grinned and began to stack some blocks. Father and son counted together ("one ... two ... three ... four ... five ...") until a tall and precarious tower stood in front of them.

"Drop it, drop it." Randy nudged Julian, encouraging him to tip the tower over. Julian gazed at his dad, his eyes twinkling with delight as Randy added a few more blocks. When the stack—and the counting—reached 16, the tower came crashing down.

"Boom!" Randy shouted.

"Boom!" Julian echoed.

Vocabulary

settle 腰を下ろす
grin にっこりする
precarious 不安定な
nudge 肘でつつく
tip over 倒す
echo おうむ返しに言う

Randy fully embraced his role as a responsive parent—so much so that he signed up for a home-visiting research program in the Chicago area to learn more about child development. (We are using only first names to protect the family's privacy.) He was tuning in to his child, talking to him, and taking turns in their ongoing conversation even though Julian couldn't say much yet. This kind of rich language input is central to the importance of nurturing relationships. For years researchers focused on the quantity of words a child heard—the so-called 30-million-word gap—as the best predictor of language development. The newest research reveals that quality of language exposure matters even more. Overhearing conversation isn't enough. Children must participate, just as Randy encouraged Julian to do.

embrace 受け入れる
so much so that ～するほどに
tune in 注意を払う
take turns 代わる代わる
so-called 30-million-word gap 「3000万語の格差」
▶この記事の読み方
predictor 予測の判断材料
exposure 触れること
matter 重要である
overhear ふと耳にする, 聞き流す

In a 2018 study, which was the first of its kind, researchers at Harvard University and the Massachusetts Institute of technology put 36 four- to six-year-old children in a brain scanner and told them stories about playing hide-and-seek and opening birthday presents. While the kids lis-

the first of its kind その種で初めて
hide-and-seek かくれんぼ

tened, the scientists looked at brain structure and function. Previously the researchers had recorded everything the children heard for two days, to get a sense of their language environment.

Children who typically experienced not just more language but more conversational turn taking showed more activation in key language areas of the brain as they heard stories in the scanner. These kids also showed stronger connections between language areas that govern speech perception and speech production. "At every socioeconomic level, more conversation was related to more mature brain development," says speech language pathologist and neuroscientist Rachel Romeo, who led the study and is now at the University of Maryland.

Other research indicates that important connections between very young children and caregivers actually occur on a neural level. Their brains sync up. Elise Piazza and her colleagues at the Princeton University Neuroscience Institute found this out when they used a method called functional near-infrared spectroscopy that can track the activity of neurons. The scientists looked at adults and infants between nine and 15 months old, in a variety of situations. The brain waves of the infants and the adult synchronized when the two were directly playing together or jointly paying attention to the same object. They did not sync when the adult spoke to someone else in the room, affirming that overheard language does not count. This kind of synchrony has been linked to social learning, problem-solving skills and vocabulary development. And when in sync, the adult turned out to be following the baby's lead, anticipating smiles and interest, rather than the other way around.

"We already knew that infant-directed speech is very important for babies' learning and that a variety of communicative cues could be important for them,"

Vocabulary

previously 前もって
get a sense of 〜の感じをつかむ

conversational turn taking 会話の順番交代
language area 言語領域
govern つかさどる, 担う
speech perception 音声認識
speech production 発話生成
socioeconomic level 社会経済レベル
pathologist 病理学者
neuroscientist 神経科学者

sync up 同期する
functional near-infrared spectroscopy 機能的近赤外分光法
neuron ニューロン, 神経細胞
synchronize (sync) 同期する
count 重要である, 意味がある
synchrony 同期性, 同調性
social learning 社会的学習
vocabulary development 語彙発達
lead 主導
the other way around その逆

infant-directed speech 対乳児発話
cue キュー（きっかけ）

says Piazza, who is now at the University of Rochester. But "even before they're fully verbal, there are a lot of ways in which [babies'] brains are picking up on these different cues in the environment."

Vocabulary

verbal 言葉を話す, 言葉を使う
pick up on ～に気づく, 理解する

Such research strongly supports the need for parents to have time with their children. It also underlines why parents also need access to high-quality, affordable child care. The problem faced by Randy, and millions like him, was that there was rarely enough time to parent the way he wished. To make ends meet, he was holding down multiple jobs. His wife, Mayra, worked full-time, too. Most days Randy saw his kids for all of 30 minutes. And the only child care Randy could afford was custodial—at pickup he often found Julian in front of a blaring television. "Here we have this body of research showing over and over that the core adult-child interactions in the early years of life are critical for brain development and social development," Romeo says. "Anything we can do as a society to create an environment where [those] relationships can flourish, that's the best investment we can make in children's futures."

underline 明確に示す
make ends meet 生計を立てる, やりくりする
hold down (職に)就く
all of たった, わずか
custodial 預かるだけの
blaring けたたましい
interactions 触れ合い, 相互作用
flourish 花開く

Early Help for Parents

Language is just one dimension of the powerful nurturing interactions between children and caregivers. For infants, connections begin on the first day of their lives. That is why paid leave at the birth of a child is consistent with policy centered on early brain development. But few Americans have such leave. Randy and Mayra didn't have it. When their two children were born, Mayra was one of the roughly one quarter of mothers who return to work within two weeks, and Randy took only a day or two off each time.

consistent with ～に沿っている, ～と一致する

Traditionally research on paid leave has focused on the economic side of the equation—assessing the impact on employers or on household incomes. Yet more recently, studies of the effects of paid leave on the health of mothers and children found it was associated with lower levels of

household incomes 家計所得, 世帯収入

postpartum depression, improved infant attachment, decreases in infant mortality and rehospitalizations, as well as increases in pediatric visits, timely immunizations and the duration of breastfeeding. When fathers took paid leave at the birth of a child, it benefited both parents' mental health, lowering depressive symptoms and stress. Plus, married parents who both take leave are less likely to divorce.

To this already persuasive evidence, the newest studies add positive impacts of paid leave on infants' cognitive development. In 2021 developmental psychologist Natalie Brito of New York University and her colleagues published a study of 328 mothers and babies from across the socioeconomic spectrum, some of whom had paid leave and some of whom had unpaid leave at the birth of their child. When the children were two years old, the researchers asked the mothers to report on their children's language abilities, as well as their emotional responses in social situations. Paid leave was associated with higher language skills for the toddlers at all socioeconomic status (SES) levels and with better emotional skills among children whose mothers had lower education levels. "It seems as though paid leave was beneficial for every family, but it may have an outsize effect for lower-SES families," Brito says.

Paid leave actually changes patterns of brain activity. In a second study of 80 mothers and babies published this past April in Child Development, Brito and her colleagues used electroencephalography (EEG) to eavesdrop on babies' brain waves three months after birth. Interactions between neurons create these waves, or oscillations. Everyone has high- and low-frequency waves, and both types are important. But as children get older, the relative amount of high-frequency activity tends to increase. Previous studies suggested that young children with more high-frequency waves, when tested a little later on in life, tend to have higher scores on skills necessary for learning and thinking.

Vocabulary

postpartum depression 産後うつ
attachment 愛着
mortality 死亡率
rehospitalization 再入院率
pediatric visit 小児科の受診
immunization 予防接種
breastfeeding 授乳
depressive symptom うつ症状

persuasive 説得力のある
developmental psychologist 発達心理学者
from across the socioeconomic spectrum さまざまな社会経済的レベルの
emotional response 情動的反応
social situation 社会的な場面
toddler よちよち歩きの子ども
outsize 特大の

electroencephalography 脳波記録法
eavesdrop on ～を傍受する，～をモニターする
interaction 相互作用
oscillation 振動
high- and low-frequency waves 高周波と低周波

In the work by Brito and her co-workers, infants whose mothers could take paid leave tended to have more higher-frequency waves, and fewer low-frequency ones, than babies whose mothers had unpaid leave. Although the sample was relatively small and not a truly random selection of babies, the researchers did control for a range of potentially confounding variables, such as gestational age at birth, number of children in the home, maternal relationship status, education and occupational prestige. The association between paid leave and brain-wave patterns persisted, explaining 12 to 30 percent of the variance in infant brain activity.

Vocabulary

confounding variable 交絡変数
gestational age 在胎週数
maternal relationship status 母親の婚姻状況
education and occupational prestige 教育・職業的地位
association 関連(性)
persist 存続する,持続する
variance 相違

It is hard to disentangle the reasons for these differences, but stress among the mothers could be one factor. The study measured levels of a stress-related hormone, cortisol, in the mothers' hair; those levels tend to go up as psychological and physical stress accumulates. Mothers who had paid leave had lower cortisol levels than mothers with unpaid leave. They also had higher parent-child interaction scores on tests of maternal sensitivity. Because paid leave provides resources and financial stability, Brito suggests, "it is likely to reduce stress and probably indirectly impacts the way that they parent or that they interact with their kids." These are the first studies of their kind and don't prove cause and effect. But, as Brito says, "some of these dots have started to be connected."

disentangle 解きほぐす,解明する
cortisol コルチゾール
accumulate 蓄積する,たまる
maternal sensitivity 母親の感受性
cause and effect 原因と結果,因果関係

米国の幼児は，その後の学校生活や人生の成功につながるいくつかの重要なスキルが他国の幼児と比べて低いという。この悩ましい情報は，経済協力開発機構（OECD）による5歳児の調査で得られたものだ。長年OECDは世界各国の15歳時点の学習到達度調査を行っており，最近調査を低年齢層に拡大した。この調査で米国の幼児は英国とエストニアの幼児に比べて読み書きや計算能力，自分の思考や行動を適切にコントロールする自己調整能力が平均して低く，協調的活動や思いやり行動，人助けのような向社会的行動も少なかった。良かったのは，感情のコントロールなどに代表される社会情動的スキルの一部が他国の幼児とほぼ同等だったことくらいだ。

調査結果は2020年3月，世界保健機関（WHO）がCOVID-19のパンデミック宣言を出した数日後に発表されたため，あまり注目を集めなかった。しかしこの結果は驚くにはあたらない。最近の別の調査でも，米国の幼児の約半数は就学準備が整わず，本来身につけておくべき重要な能力の発達に遅れが見られた。OECDの調査が就学前の幼児を対象にしている点は，われわれが見失っていた基本的なことを強く思い出させる。それは，子どもの学習が就学1日目でなく，生後1日目から始まるということだ。子ども時代の最初の数年間はチャンスに満ちている。子どもの脳が体験を最も柔軟に受け入れ，可塑性に富んでいるのが，この最初の重要な時期だ。脳の成長の85%は生まれてから3歳までの間に起こる。この時期には毎秒100万個の神経接続が形成されている。

20年に及ぶ子どもの発達研究から，幼児が最高の成長のスタートを切るには「養育者との親密な関わり」と「有害なストレスからの保護」の2つが何よりも大切であることがわかった。さらに，早期の幼児体験が脳に及ぼす神経生理学的な影響を探った最近5年間の新たな研究が，この2つの目標を達成する方法をはっきりと示している。こうした研究から，幼児の脳内で何が起きているかを垣間見ることができる。幼児の発達に良いことが知られてきた育児環境や養育者との相互作用が，実際に脳内でも言語や認知の発達を担う領域の神経活動や接続を高めることが明らかになっている。

著者の1人（サスキンド）は小児科医で幼児教育の研究者でもあり，脳の発達に関する最新の科学的知見を親の行動だけでなく社会の変革に生かす方法を探っている。例えば，有給休暇があれば，親は子どもとの人間関係を育む時間を持てる。児童手当や税額控除があれば，子どもの成長に悪影響を及ぼす貧困を軽減できる。米国の多くのケースがそうであるように，両親が外に出て働いている場合，質の高い保育所を利用できれば，幼児としっかり触れ合う熱心な保育士に子どもを預けることができる。

しかし実際には，科学的に見て子どもに必要な支援と，われわれの社会が提供している支援には隔たりがある。米国は産後の育児休業制度を義務付けていない唯一の先進国である。2020 年には米国の子どもの 4 割が生活必需品の購

この記事の読み方

子育て支援が子どもの認知発達にどのような影響をおよぼすかを神経科学的な観点から論じた記事である。とくに貧困家庭においては，経済的支援が子どもの認知発達に実効性をもつことが強調されている。原題は "The Path to Better Childhoods"（よりよい幼年期への道）。邦題は「子育て支援の神経科学」という具体性をもったタイトルにしてある。

乳幼児の認知発達（とくに言語の発達）において重要なのは，養育者との interaction（相互作用／関わり／触れ合い）である。このためには，養育者は十分な時間をとる必要があるが，職業的・経済的制約からそれができない家庭がある。では，国として，社会として，どんな支援ができるか。それが本記事の読みどころだ。

so-called 30-million-word gap（「3000 万語の格差」）は，家庭内で子どもに話しかける単語の述べ数を最多と最少の家庭で比較すると，3 歳の終わりまでに 3000 万語の違いになるというセンセーショナルな研究結果にもとづく。ただし記事のなかでは，重要なのは言語体験の量ではなく，質だということも強調されている。

この記事がきわめて重要であるのは，科学的データを提示しながら，産後の育児休業制度や児童税額控除など，米国政府がとるべき子育て支援の施策について具体的な提言を行っている点。いまの日本にもそっくりあてはまる問題である。

入もままならない家庭で暮らしていた。また，米国議会は児童税額控除の拡充を延長しない道を選んだ。パンデミック対策として拡充されていたこの税額控除は何百万もの家庭を助け，子どもの貧困者数を大幅に減らすのに役立っていたというのに。さらに，米国人の約半分が保育施設と人材がまったく不足している“保育砂漠”地域に住んでいるほか，既存の保育サービスのうち質が高いものは10%に満たないと考えられている。パンデミックはこれらのギャップを浮き彫りにし，米国の子育て支援の脆弱さを露呈した。

脳の発達に関する科学は，こうした問題に取り組む議論においてほとんど扱われることがない。だがこれからは議論の中心に据えるべきだ。なぜなら，最新の科学的知見は子どもの将来を大きく改善するために国や地方が何をすべきかを明確に示しているからだ。

言語体験は「量」よりも「質」

ランディはお気に入りのシカゴ・ブルズの帽子をかぶり，リビングルームの柔らかなカーペットに座って2歳の息子ジュリアンを引き寄せて膝に乗せた。「遊ぼうか？」と言うと，ジュリアンはにこっと笑って積み木を積み始めた。父と息子は「ひとつ，ふたつ，みっつ……」と数えながら積んでいき，高くなった塔はぐらぐらし始めた。

「倒せ！倒せ！」とランディがジュリアンをつついて促すと，ジュリアンは父親の顔をじっと見つめた。ランディがさらにいくつか積んでいくと，ジュリアンは嬉しそうに目を輝かせた。16個目を積んだときに，ついに塔ががらがらと倒れた。「バーン！」とランディが叫ぶと，「バーン！」とジュリアンもまねをした。

ランディは子どもとしっかり触れ合う父親の役割をちゃんと心得ている。それもそのはず，彼は子どもの発達についての理解を深めることを目的としたシカゴ地区の家庭訪問プログラムに登録した1人だ。彼は子どもに注意を払って自分から話しかけ，ジュリアンがまだ多くを話せないのに2人の間で会話が続くようにした。この種の豊かな言語的インプットこそが，子育ての触れ合いで最も重要だ。長年，研究者は幼児が聞いた単語の「量」が言語発達に最も影響を与えるとみて注目してきた。いわゆる「3000万語の格差」である。しかし，最新の研究から言語体験の「質」がより重要であることがわかった。会話を聞き流すだけでは不十分なのだ。ランディがジュリアンに仕向けたように，子ども自身が会話に参加しなければならない。

2018年にハーバード大学とマサチューセッツ工科大学のチームが，話を聞いている子どもの脳の構造と機能をfMRI（機能的磁気共鳴画像装置）で調べて比較する初の研究を行った。4～6歳の36人にfMRIへ入ってもらい，かくれんぼや誕生日プレゼントを開ける話を聞かせた。実験に先立ち，子どもたちの言語環境を知るために，彼らが生活の中で聞いた音を2日間にわたってすべて録音した。

fMRIの装置内で話を聞いている間，脳内の主要な言語領域がより活発に働いていたのは，生活の中で単に多くの言葉を聞いていただけではなく，より多くの会話に参加していた子どもたちだった。また，これらの子どもたちは，言語領域の中で「音声認識」と「発話生成」を担う部分の間により強い接続を示した。「子どもの育つ家庭の社会経済レベルに関係なく，より多くの会話への参加が脳発達の高い成熟度と関連していた」と，この研究を主導し，現在はメリーランド大学にいる言語病理学者で神経科学者のロミオ（Rachel Romeo）は言う。

別の研究では，1歳前後の乳幼児と養育者との間の強い結びつきが実際に神経レベルで起こっていることが示された。両者の脳が“同期”するのだ。プリンストン大学神経科学研究所のピアザ（Elise Piazza）らはfNIRS（機能的近赤外分光法）を用い，大人と9～15月齢の乳幼児を対象にさまざまな状況下で神経活動を追跡した。乳幼児と大人が直接一緒に遊んでいるときや，同じものに一緒に注目しているときに2人の脳波は同期した。一方，大人が同じ室内の他の人に話しかけているときには同期せず，ただの立ち聞きにはあまり意味がないことを裏づけた。このような脳波の同期は，社会的学習や問題解決能力，語彙発達と関連することが知られている。また，同期が起こるのは，会話の主導権が赤ちゃんにあって大人の方は赤ちゃんの笑顔や関心が自分に向けられるのを期待しているときであって，その逆ではなかった。

「対乳児発話という抑揚をつけた話し方やコミュニケーションの“キュー”（きっかけ）を作ることが乳児の学習に重要であることがすでに知られていたが，まだうまく話せない段階でも乳児の脳は周囲のさまざまなキューを拾っていることがわかった」と，現在はロチェスター大学にいるピアザは言う。

これらの研究結果は親子が一緒に過ごす時間の必要性を強く示しており，質が高く誰でも利用可能な保育所が必要な理由でもある。ランディのような何百万人もの親たちが直面している問題は，自分の望む方法で子育てをする時間がほとんどないことだ。ランディは生活をやりくりするために複数の仕事をこなし，妻のマイラもフルタイムで働いていた。ランディが子どもと過ごす時間は毎日たったの 30 分だった。そしてランディが金銭的に利用可能だった保育所は子どもを預かるだけで，迎えに行くとジュリアンは大音量のテレビの前にいることが少なくなかった。「一連の研究成果が繰り返し訴えているのは，人生のごく初期における大人と子どもの十分な触れ合いが脳の発達と社会性の形成に不可欠であるということだ」とロミオは言う。「そのような豊かな触れ合いを育む環境を作るために社会全体が取り組むことが，子どもの未来のための最善の投資だ」。

出生 1 日目からの育児支援を

言語は子どもと養育者の活発な触れ合いにおける 1 つの側面にすぎず，乳児は出生 1 日目から周囲とつながりを持ち始めている。したがって出産日から始まる有給の産後休業は，子どもの脳の発達に重要だといえる。しかし，米国で現在そのような休業を取得できる人はほとんどいない。ランディとマイラも例外ではない。2 人の子が生まれた際，マイラは米国の母親たちの約 1/4 と同じく 2 回とも 2 週間以内に職場復帰し，ランディも 1 ～ 2 日休んだだけだった。

有給の産後休業が持つ効果についての研究はこれまで経済的側面，つまり雇用主や家庭の収入への影響のみに焦点を当ててきた。しかし最近では母子の健康への効果も調べられている。有給の産後休業は産後うつを低減し，乳児と母親の間の愛着を強めることが明らかになった。さらに，乳児の死亡率と再入院率の低下や，小児科の受診の増加，スケジュール通りの予防接種の実施，母乳育児期間の増加といった効果もあった。また，父親が子どもの出生に際して有給で休業することにより，両親ともにうつ症状やストレスが軽減されて心の健康状態が向上した。夫婦がともに有給の休業を取得した場合には離婚率も下がった。

これらの説得力のある結果に加え，最新の研究から有給の産後休業が幼児の認知発達に好影響を与えることもわかった。2021年，ニューヨーク大学の発達心理学者ブリトー（Natalie Brito）らは328人の母と子を対象に，有給と無給の産後休業が子どもの発達にどのような影響を与えるかを調べた。さまざまな社会経済的レベルの人を調査対象とし，子どもが2歳になったときの言語能力ならびに人に対する情動的反応について母親から報告してもらった。その結果，有給の産後休業を取得した家庭では，親の社会経済的レベルとは関係なく，幼児の言語能力スコアが高かった。さらに母親の受けた教育レベルが低い家庭では，有給の産後休業を取った場合の方が情動を制御する能力のスコアが向上していた。「有給の産後休業は全ての家庭に恩恵をもたらすようだが，親の教育レベルが低い家庭では特に効果が大きいとみられる」とブリトーは言う。

有給の産後休業は実際に脳の活動パターンを変化させる。ブリトーらはさらに脳波検査の手法を用いて生後3カ月の乳児の脳活動を調べ，その結果を2022年4月の *Child Development* 誌に発表した。脳波は神経細胞間の相互作用によって生じるもので，誰の脳波にも高周波と低周波の成分が含まれる。どちらの脳波も重要だが，子どもが成長するにつれて高周波の比率が高くなる傾向がある。また以前の研究から，幼少期に高周波の比率が高かった子どもは，のちに学習や思考に必要な能力が高まる傾向が示されている。

ブリトーらの研究の結果，母親が有給の産後休業を取った家庭の乳児では，産後休業が無給だった母親の子と比べて脳波に含まれる高周波の比率が高く，低周波の比率が低い傾向が見られた。この研究の対象者数はやや少なく，サンプルの抽出も完全なランダムではないものの，乳児の在胎週数やきょうだいの数，母親の婚姻状況と教育・職業的地位など，交絡因子となりうるさまざまな要因を考慮した補正はしっかり行った。そうした補正のうえで，乳児の脳活動の違いの12～30%を有給の産後休業を取ったかどうかで説明できることが示された。

脳波の差が生まれる仕組みを明らかにするのは容易ではないが，1つの要因は母親のストレスかもしれない。この研究では母親の髪の毛を用いてストレス関連ホルモンであるコルチゾールの値も調べた。コルチゾールは心理的または身体的なストレスの蓄積にともなって増える傾向がある。有給の産後休業を取得した母親は無給の産後休業を取得した母親に比べてコルチゾール値が低く，また，母親の感受性テストでは親子の交流を示すスコアが高かった。有給の産後休業は経済的安定性の確保につながるため，「ストレスが軽減され，間接的に子育ての仕方や子との接し方に影響を与えるのではないか」とブリトーは推測する。こうした手法の研究はまだ少なく，因果関係を証明したものではないが，ブリトーは「これらの事実につながりが見え始めている」と話す。

Dana Suskind／Lydia Denworth
サスキンドは幼児教育研究者。米シカゴ大学メディカルセンターの小児人工内耳インプラント外科医で，「早期学習と公衆衛生のための TMW センター」の共同ディレクター。デンワースは米ニューヨーク州ブルックリンを拠点とするサイエンスライターで，SCIENTIFIC AMERICAN 誌の寄稿編集者。サスキンドとデンワースの共著書に “Parent Nation: Unlocking Every Child’s Potential, Fulfilling Society’s Promise”（Dutton，2022）がある。

When Pretending Is the Remedy

プラセボ効果の脳科学

T. グーラ
（サイエンスライター）

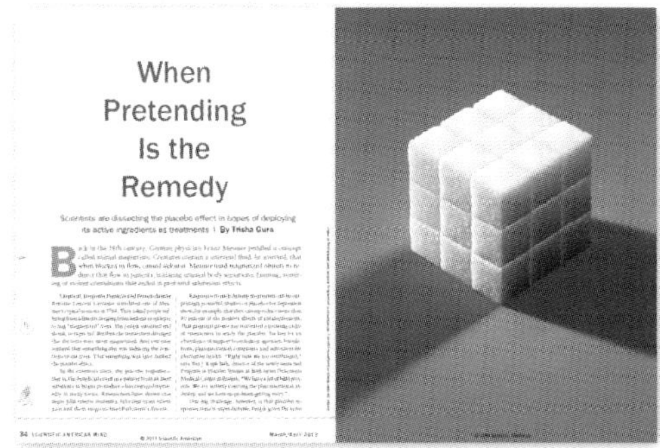
When Pretending Is the Remedy

Scientists are dissecting the placebo effect in hopes of deploying its active ingredients as treatments | By Trisha Gura

プラセボ効果が持つ力を新たな治療法として使えないだろうか
そんな期待のもと，詳しい研究が進んでいる

KEY CONCEPTS

何もないものの背後にある何か

- ■偽の治療が驚くほど効くことがある。うつ病に対する偽薬の効果が，抗うつ剤を使う場合の80%を超える例がある。
- ■偽薬は，脳において期待や注意，情動をつかさどる各回路を働かせる。
- ■将来，医師たちは日常的に偽薬を使い，承認薬や治療法の効果を増し，場合によっては偽薬がそうした薬剤や治療法に取って代わるかもしれない。

日経サイエンス 2014年2月号，SCIENTIFIC AMERICAN MIND March/April 2013

Back in the 18th century, German physician Franz Mesmer peddled a concept called animal magnetism. Creatures contain a universal fluid, he asserted, that when blocked in flow, caused sickness. Mesmer used magnetized objects to redirect that flow in patients, initiating unusual body sensations, fainting, vomiting or violent convulsions that ended in profound salubrious effects.

Skeptical, Benjamin Franklin and French chemist Antoine-Laurent Lavoisier simulated one of Mesmer's typical sessions in 1784. They asked people suffering from ailments ranging from asthma to epilepsy to hug "magnetized" trees. The people swooned and shook, as expected. But then the researchers divulged that the trees were never magnetized. And everyone realized that something else was inducing the reactions to the trees. That something was later dubbed the placebo effect.

In the centuries since, the placebo response—that is, the beneficial result in a patient from an inert substance or bogus procedure—has emerged repeatedly in many forms. Researchers have shown that sugar pills reverse insomnia, fake injections relieve pain and sham surgeries treat Parkinson's disease.

Responses to such dummy treatments can be surprisingly powerful. Studies on placebos for depression show, for example, that they can reproduce more than 80 percent of the positive effects of antidepressants. That potential power has motivated a growing cadre of researchers to study the placebo, backed by an abundance of support from federal agencies, foundations, pharmaceutical companies and advocates for alternative health. "Right now we are overfunded," says Ted J. Kaptchuk, director of the newly launched Program in Placebo Studies at Beth Israel Deaconess Medical Center in Boston. "We have a lot of NIH projects. We are actively courting the pharmaceutical industry, and we have no problem getting entry."

Vocabulary

[タイトル] **pretend** （本物だと）偽る，ふりをする
remedy 治療，治療法，治療薬

physician 医師
peddle 広める，説いて回る
animal magnetism 動物磁気
creature 生物
universal fluid 共通の流体
assert 主張する
magnetized 磁気を帯びた
initiate 引き起こす
body sensation 身体感覚
fainting 失神
vomiting 嘔吐
convulsion 痙攣
profound 広範囲の
salubrious 健康に良い

skeptical 懐疑的な
ailment 病気
asthma 喘息
epilepsy てんかん
swoon 気絶する
shake 痙攣する
divulge 打ち明ける
induce 誘発する
dub 名付ける
placebo effect プラセボ（偽薬）効果
▶この記事の読み方

placebo response プラセボ反応
inert substance 不活性物質
bogus procedure 偽の処置
sugar pill 砂糖の錠剤
reverse 好転させる
insomnia 不眠症
fake injection 偽の注射
sham 偽の

depression うつ病
reproduce 再現する
antidepressant 抗うつ剤
cadre 集団
back 支援する
advocate 支持者
alternative health 代替医療

One big challenge, however, is that placebo responses remain unpredictable. People given the same pill or potion may show wildly different reactions. The effects can vary widely by illness. Pain, insomnia, fatigue, nausea, and disturbances to bowel, urinary or sexual function seem the most amenable to placebo treatments; broken limbs the least. Attempts to explain such variation have led scientists to delve deeper into the nature of the placebo effect. They have found that it shows up most prominently in illnesses that have a strong psychological component or when improvement is measured using subjective reports from patients.

With better neuroimaging tools and more sophisticated experimental designs, investigators are deconstructing placebo responses in the brain. They are finding that placebos can tap circuits governing expectation, attention and emotion. A placebo's power in these realms depends on social and environmental cues that act around the dummy pill, prick or potion. The doctor's behavior, for example, plays an essential role. "The placebo is about the terrain of medicine," Kaptchuk observes. "What things are said; how the doctor behaves. It's the rituals and symbols—sitting in the waiting room, the patient exam, et cetera. And then, at the psychological level, it is the active ingredients of hope and trust and imagination, which are really antithetical to a scientific world."

Doctors hope to use this antithetical collection of findings to predict when and where a placebo will work and enhance its benefits in the clinic—ideally without deception. As the data reveal the biological mechanisms behind these "sham" remedies, placebos may become standard medical fare, used to augment and, in some cases, replace approved drugs and therapies. Incurable conditions, such as chronic pain, asthma and Alzheimer's disease, may one day yield to placebos, Kaptchuk suggests. Mesmer's idea of animal magnetism may have been bunk, but what

Vocabulary

NIH 国立衛生研究所
court （支援・支持を）求める，働きかける
entry 参加

potion （薬の）一服
nausea 吐き気
disturbance 障害
bowel 腸
urinary 泌尿器の
amenable 従順な，効き目がある
limb 四肢，手足
delve 探る，掘り下げる
prominently 顕著に
psychological component 心理的要素
subjective 主観的な

neuroimaging 脳画像検査
deconstruct 分析する
tap 活性化する
govern つかさどる
emotion 情動
realm 領域
social and environmental cues 社会・環境条件
prick （針で）刺すこと
terrain 領域
medicine 医術
observe 言う，意見を述べる
ritual 儀式
active ingredient 活性（有効）成分
antithetical 正反対の，対極にある

deception だますこと
fare メニュー
augment 拡大する
incurable condition 不治の病
yield to 屈する，克服される
bunk たわごと
inadvertently 気づかずに

he inadvertently tapped was not.

Subjective Salve

Placebos debuted in contemporary medical research, not as objects of study but as tools for clinical experiments. In 1955 Harvard Medical School physician Henry K. Beecher published a landmark report in which he estimated that 35 percent of any treatment group responded to a placebo. Entitled "The Powerful Placebo," the study offered evidence from 15 clinical trials of 1,082 patients to back up his claims of the existence of a placebo effect. He pushed for trials that compared patients taking drugs with those taking placebos. Only in 1968 did the Food and Drug Administration formally usher placebos into standard clinical trials as a way of ensuring that drugs worked as manufacturers claimed.

Meanwhile astute practitioners such as Kaptchuk were noticing something mysterious happening with their patients. Perhaps the most unusual associate professor at Harvard Medical School, Kaptchuk holds no Ph.D. or M.D. Instead, after graduating from Columbia University in 1968, he took off for Macao, China, earned a doctor of Oriental medicine (OMD) degree in 1975 and began to practice acupuncture a year later. After 15 years, he realized that the needles themselves could not account for the curative effects of his practice. He quit and set out to explore what else was helping his patients feel better.

In studies conducted over two decades, Kaptchuk and others found that Beecher's initial estimates were flawed. For starters, Beecher had not separated patients' responses to the placebo from other phenomena, such as the fact that some patients simply got better with time. Even more curious, different placebos worked optimally for different ailments. Pills worked better for insomnia, for example, whereas shots provided the best pain relief. And placebo effects could occur by proxy. For instance, parents

Vocabulary

tap 利用する

salve 慰め，癒やし
debut デビューする，初登場する
landmark 画期的な
clinical trial 臨床試験，治験
back up 裏づける
push for ～を推す
only ようやく
usher something into ～に導入する

meanwhile 一方で
astute 目ざとい，目先の利く
practitioner 医療従事者，施術者
take off for ～へと旅立つ
Oriental medicine 東洋医学，漢方
acupuncture 鍼治療
account for ～の主要因である，～を説明する
curative effect 治療効果
practice 施術
set out to ～し始める，～に乗り出す

flawed 欠点のある
for starters まず第一に
curious 好奇心をそそる，奇異な
optimally 最適に
shot 注射
pain relief 鎮痛，痛みの軽減
by proxy 代理人を通して

can help their child get better simply by feeling positive about their child's prescription.

Just as placebo studies seemed to be gathering force, in 2001 a Danish group dropped a bombshell. Epidemiologist Asbjørn Hróbjartsson of the Nordic Cochrane Center in Copenhagen and his colleagues conducted a meta-analysis in which they reviewed 114 trials that investigated 40 clinical conditions. In each, patients randomly received either a placebo or no treatment. Investigators found little evidence that placebos had significant clinical effects. Yet in that study, entitled "Is the Placebo Powerless?" and in two others published in 2004 and 2010, Hróbjartsson also found incredible variability in placebo responses. "We are seeing a dramatic effect in some laboratories and trials but lack of effect in others," he says.

One source of that variability was in how researchers tracked improvement. If doctors measured success by medical, objective measures such as blood pressure, placebos did not appear to work. But in certain settings, if researchers tracked recovery by how patients reported they felt, then placebos revealed their potency, especially in conditions such as pain and nausea.

Indeed, in 2002 Harvard psychologist Irving Kirsch found results consistent with the idea that the power of placebos is evident mostly when improvement is subjective, as it is in mental illness. In a meta-analysis of 47 trials of six of the most widely prescribed antidepressants, Kirsch and his colleagues discovered that 82 percent of the improvement in mood, as measured by a standard questionnaire, could be duplicated by giving patients a placebo pill instead of an antidepressant. In a similar study published in 2008, Kirsch and his colleagues found that the only people in whom antidepressants worked significantly better than placebo pills were patients with the most severe cases. He reached a controversial conclusion: "Unless your patient

Vocabulary

prescription 処方, 処方薬

gather force 勢力を増す
bombshell 爆弾
epidemiologist 疫学者
meta-analysis メタ解析
▶この記事の読み方
clinical condition 臨床症状
significant 有意な, 大きな
variability ばらつき

source 原因
objective measure 客観的な尺度
potency 効能, 有効性

consistent with ～と一致する
evident 明白な, 明らかな
prescribed 処方された
mood 気分
questionnaire 質問紙
duplicate 繰り返す
controversial 物議をかもす

is extremely depressed, you shouldn't be prescribing an antidepressant."

Placebos also seem to work on a subjective level in nonpsychiatric conditions, such as asthma. In a 2011 study Kaptchuk, Kirsch and their colleagues gave 46 volunteers with asthma either an inhaler with a drug (albuterol), an inhaler with saline, sham acupuncture or nothing. During each of 12 visits, researchers measured how much air the patients could inhale and exhale, both before and after treatment. The respiratory scores of those treated with albuterol rose by 20 percent, whereas all the others got just a 7 percent bump, suggesting the placebos had no effect.

But when the researchers asked the asthma sufferers to rank their respiratory discomfort on a scale of 0 to 10, everyone except those who got no treatment reported a 50 percent improvement. Even though the drug was causing a "robust" medical effect, as compared with the placebo, patients could not reliably detect the difference. Perhaps the placebo activates a mechanism that is distinct from the pharmaceutical's targeted pathway but, in some respects, is equally effective. "A medical treatment has two components: the actual pharmacological effect and the placebo component of the active treatment," Kirsch says.

Vocabulary

nonpsychiatric condition 精神疾患以外の症状
inhaler 吸入器
albuterol アルブテロール
saline 生理食塩水
inhale 吸う
exhale 吐く
respiratory 呼吸の

discomfort 不快症状
robust 力強い, 頑健な
distinct from ～とは異なる
pharmaceutical's targeted pathway 薬が狙う経路
in some respects いくつかの点で
pharmacological 薬理学的な

18世紀，ドイツ人医師のメスメル（Franz Mesmer）は動物磁気という概念を喧伝して回った。生物はみな，ある共通の液体が体内にあり，その流れが滞ると病気になると主張した。メスメルは，磁気を帯びた器具を用いて患者の体内のこの流れを変えることで，異様な身体感覚を覚えさせたり，失神や嘔吐，あるいはひどい痙攣を起こさせ，その結果心身の状態を劇的に改善させた。

フランクリン（Benjamin Franklin）とフランスの化学者ラボアジェ（Antoine-Laurent Lavoisier）はこれに疑いを抱いた。彼らは1784年，メスメルが行っていた典型的な手技の1つを試してみた。喘息やてんかんなどの症状がある人に“磁気を帯びた木”を両腕でしっかりと抱いてもらったのだ。指示通りにした人たちは予想通り，気絶したり痙攣を起こしたりした。その後，フランクリンたちはその木は実はまったく磁気など帯びていないとタネ明かしした。こうして人々の木に対する反応を引き起こしたのは別の何かであることがわかり，これが「プラセボ（偽薬）効果」と名付けられた。

このプラセボ反応（何の有効成分もない物質や偽の処置によって患者に生じる有益な結果）は，その後数世紀にわたり，繰り返し形を変えて登場した。砂糖の錠剤が不眠を治し，偽の注射が痛みを緩和し，見せかけの手術がパーキンソン病の症状を改善することなどが示されてきた。

このようなダミー治療の効き目は，時には驚くほど強力だ。例えばうつ病の治療で，抗うつ剤による治療効果の80%以上をプラセボ効果で実現できることを示した複数の報告がある。こうした期待から，偽薬の研究に携わる人が増え，連邦機関や財団，製薬会社，代替医療の支持者から多額の支援が寄せられている。ボストンにあるベス・イスラエル・ディーコネス・メディカルセンターで始まった「プラセボ研究プログラム」のリーダーであるカプチャク（Ted J. Kaptchuk）は「我々は十分すぎるほどの資金提供を受けている」と言う。「国立衛生研究所（NIH）の助成プロジェクトが多数あり，製薬業界からも熱い支援を得ている。試験への参加者集めにも苦労はない」。

ただ，問題もある。依然としてこのプラセボ反応が予測不能であることだ。同一の錠剤や薬剤を与えても，反応は人によって大きく異なる。病気の種類による違いも大きい。痛みや不眠，疲労，吐き気，腸や泌尿器機能，性機能の障害などは偽薬治療の効き目が大きい半面，手足の骨折などへの効果はあまりない。この理由を知るためプラセボ効果の性質が詳しく調べられてきた。その結果，プラセボ効果は心理的要素が強い病気の場合や，患者の主観的な回答から改善効果を測定する時に顕著に表れることがわかった。

新鋭の脳画像検査や精密な実験によって，偽薬に対する脳の反応が調べられた。その結果，期待や注意，情動をつかさどる脳内の各回路が偽薬によって活性化することがわかった。また，そうした効果は偽薬を与えるときの社会・環境条件に左右されるようだ。医師がどのように振る舞うかはとりわけ重要だ。「偽薬は医術の問題なのだ」とカプチャクは話す。「患者が何を言われ，医者がどんな態度をとるか。患者が待合室で座って待ち，検査を受けるなどはいわば一連の儀式であり，象徴的な意味を持つ。患者の期待感や信頼感，想像力を形成する心理的要素となる。実際のところ科学とは相反する世界なのだ」。

医師たちは，この科学とは相反する一連の所見を用いつつ，偽薬がいつ，どのような場合に効き，実際の治療に役立てられる（理想を言えば患者を欺かずに）のかを予測したいと考えている。“見せかけ”の治療法の背後にある生物学的メカニズムがデータから明らかになれば，プラセボは標準的な医療となり，既存の薬剤や治療法の効果を高め，場合によっては取って代わるかもしれない。カプチャクは，慢性の痛みや喘息，アルツハイマー病など不治の病が将来，偽薬によって克服されるかもしれないという。メスメルが唱えた動物磁気はたわごとだったようだが，彼が偶然利用していた効果はでたらめではなかったというわけだ。

患者だけが感じる癒し

偽薬は研究対象としてではなく，臨床試験の道具として現代医学の舞台に登場した。1955年，ハーバード大学医学部の医師ビーチャー（Henry K. Beecher）は，いかなる治療群も35%が偽薬に反応するという画期的な報告を発表した。「強力な偽薬」と題したこの報告は，15 件の臨床試験における 1082 の患者例から，プラセボ効果の存在を裏づける証拠を得た。ビーチャーは薬を服用した患者と偽薬を服用した患者を比較する臨床試験を推奨した。しかし，薬剤がメーカーの主張通りに作用するかどうかを確認する方法として米食品医薬品局（FDA）が偽薬を標準的な臨床試験に導入したのは，1968 年になってからのことだった。

一方で，カプチャクのような目先の利く現場の関係者は，自分の患者に不思議なことが起こるのに気づいていた。ハーバード大学医学部の恐らく最も変わった准教授であるカプチャクは博士号も医師免許も持っていない。彼は 1968 年にコロンビア大学を卒業後，中国のマカオに飛び，1975 年に東洋医の資格をと

この記事の読み方

placebo effect（プラセボ効果／偽薬効果）とは，薬効のないニセの薬を薬効があると偽って処方しても，効果が見られることをいう。本記事は，この効果が顕著に現れるのがどのような病気の場合か，それには脳のどの領域が関与しているかという研究を紹介している。記事の原題は “When Pretending Is the Remedy”（ふりをすることが治療薬になる時）。

記事は，18 世紀のメスメルの動物磁気説とフランクリンやラボアジェの反証実験の話から始まっている。国の異なる有名なこの 3 人を登場させたのは，200 年以上も前に欧米ではプラセボ効果が大きな関心を集めていたということを強調したかったからだろう。しかし現在も，この効果の生起メカニズムについては不明なことが多い。

公表されている多数の研究のデータを集約して再分析するのが meta analysis。「メタ分析」や「メタ解析」と訳されるが，統計的な色彩が強い場合にはメタ解析と訳したほうがよいかもしれない。

なお，プラセボ効果（あるいは本物の薬自体の薬効）を調べる実験では通常，被験者がどの実験条件（本物か偽薬か）に割り振られているかが，被験者だけでなく実験者にもわからないようにして行われる。

ると 1 年後に鍼療法を始めた。15 年後，自分の施術の効果が鍼では説明できないと悟り，診療をやめ，患者の具合がよくなるのに他の何が効いているのかを研究し始めた。

20 年間にわたる研究の中で，カプチャクらはビーチャーの当初の推定に問題があることに気づいた。ビーチャーは，偽薬に対する患者の反応と，時とともに症状が自然に改善するといった現象を分けて考えていなかった。さらに奇妙なことに，偽薬の種類によって効く病気が異なっていた。例えば，不眠症には錠剤がよく効くのに対して，痛みを和らげるには注射の効果が最も大きかった。また，プラセボ効果は本人以外の力で生じることがあった。例えば，親が自分の子に処方されている薬に肯定的な気持ちを持つだけで，子の症状が改善されたりした。

偽薬の研究が盛んになりつつあった 2001 年，デンマークのある研究グループが衝撃的な発表をした。コペンハーゲンのノルディック・コクラン・センターの疫学者フロブヤートソン（Asbjørn Hróbjartsson）らはメタ解析の手法を使い，40 の臨床症状に関する 114 件の試験を検討した。それらの臨床試験はいずれも，患者を偽薬投与と何も治療しない群に無作為に振り分けて比較したものだ。メタ解析の結果，偽薬が大きな臨床効果を及ぼすことを裏づける証拠はないと判明した。もっとも，「偽薬は無力か」と題されたこの報告および 2004 年と 2010 年に報告された別の 2 つの論文で，フロブヤートソンはプラセボ反応に甚だしいばらつきがあることも見いだした。「研究室や試験によっては劇的な効果が見られるのに，他の例ではまるで効果がない」という。

こうしたばらつきの原因の 1 つは，研究者が症状改善を追跡する方法の違いに関係していた。例えば血圧といった客観的な医学的尺度で治療の成否を測定した場合，偽薬には効果がないように思われた。しかし，特定の設定で，患者自身からの聞き取りで回復具合を追跡した場合には効果が見られた。特に痛みや吐き気などの病状への効果は大きかった。

実際，2002年にハーバード大学の心理学者カーシュ（Irving Kirsch）は，プラセボ効果が精神疾患のように改善が主観的なものである時に最もよく観察されることを支持する複数の試験結果を見いだした。広く処方されている抗うつ薬6種類に関する試験47件に関してメタ解析を行い，標準的な質問紙による回答で測定した気分の改善のうち82%は，患者に抗うつ薬でなく偽薬錠を投与しても同様の改善があることを見いだした。2008年に発表したこれと類似の研究で，カーシュらは偽の錠剤よりも抗うつ薬の効果の方が明らかに大きかったのは，極めて重度の患者だけだったことを突き止めた。こうしてカーシュは「患者が極度のうつ状態でない限り，抗うつ薬を処方すべきではない」という，物議をかもす結論に達した。

喘息のような精神疾患以外の症状にも，偽薬は主観的な効果をもたらすようだ。2011年，カプチャクとカーシュらは，喘息の被験者46人を対象に，①薬剤（気管支拡張剤のアルブテロール）の入った吸入器を使う，②生理食塩水の入った吸入器を使う，③偽の鍼治療を行う，④何もしないの4つを比較試験した。試験中，患者は計12回来院し，治療前後の呼吸能力を比較した。本物の薬剤を投与した患者は呼吸スコアが20%上昇したのに対して，他の患者はいずれもスコアの上昇が7%にとどまった。このことは偽薬がまったく作用していないことを示唆する。

ところが，喘息患者に自分の呼吸器の不快症状を0～10の段階で評価するように求めると，何もしなかった患者を除く全員が「50%改善した」と回答した。薬剤が偽薬と比較して医学的に“明確な”効果を発揮しているのに，患者はその差を確実には知覚できなかったわけだ。おそらく偽薬は，通常の薬が狙う経路とは異なるが，いくつかの点で同等の効果を持つメカニズムを作動させている。「薬物療法は，実際の薬理作用と，治療行為をすることに伴うプラセボ効果という2つの要素からなる」とカーシュは言う。

Trisha Gura
米ボストンに拠点を置くサイエンスライター。

Making AI More Human

子どもの脳に学ぶ AI

A. ゴプニック
(米カリフォルニア大学バークレー校)

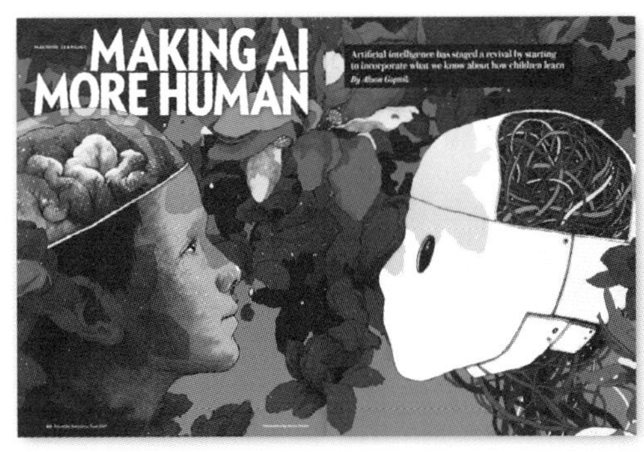

子どもの学習の仕方に関する知見が
人工知能の華々しい復活をもたらした

KEY CONCEPTS

人間に近い2方向の学習法

■幼児はどのように知識を獲得するのか？　長きにわたって哲学者や心理学者を虜にしてきたこの問いに，いまコンピューター科学者も挑んでいる。

■人工知能（AI）の専門家は世の中のさまざまなことを機械に教える方法を開発するために，未就学児の推論能力について研究している。

■2つの競合する機械学習法によって，学問分野としてのAIが一変し始めた。どちらも子どもが自然に行っていることを不完全ながらまねるものだ。

日経サイエンス 2018 年 2 月号，SCIENTIFIC AMERICAN June 2017

If you spend much time with children, you're bound to wonder how young human beings can possibly learn so much so quickly. Philosophers, going all the way back to Plato, have wondered, too, but they've never found a satisfying answer. My five-year-old grandson, Augie, has learned about plants, animals and clocks, not to mention dinosaurs and spaceships. He also can figure out what other people want and how they think and feel. He can use that knowledge to classify what he sees and hears and make new predictions. He recently proclaimed, for example, that the newly discovered species of titanosaur on display at the American Museum of Natural History in New York City is a plant eater, so that means it really isn't that scary.

Yet all that reaches Augie from his environment is a stream of photons hitting his retina and disturbances of air contacting his eardrums. The neural computer that sits behind his blue eyes manages somehow to start with that limited information from his senses and to end up making predictions about plant-eating titanosaurs. One lingering question is whether electronic computers can do the same.

During the past 15 years or so computer scientists and psychologists have been trying to find an answer. Children acquire a great deal of knowledge with little input from teachers or parents. Despite enormous strides in machine intelligence, even the most powerful computers still cannot learn as well as a five-year-old does.

Figuring out how the child brain actually functions—and then creating a digital version that will work as effectively—will challenge computer scientists for decades to come. But in the meantime, they are beginning to develop artificial intelligence that incorporates some of what we know about how humans learn.

Vocabulary

be bound to ～するに決まっている，～せずにはいられない
Plato プラトン
figure out 理解する
proclaim 言い放つ
titanosaur ティタノサウルス
plant eater 草食動物
scary 恐ろしい，怖い

photon 光子
retina 網膜
disturbance 乱れ，振動
eardrum 鼓膜
neural computer 神経コンピューター
sense 感覚
lingering 長く続く，長年の

machine intelligence 機械知能

challenge ～の課題となる
for decades to come 今後数十年にわたって
in the meantime さしあたり
artificial intelligence 人工知能
incorporate 組み込む

This Way Up

After the first burst of enthusiasm in the 1950s and 1960s, the quest for AI languished for decades. In the past few years, though, there have been striking advances, especially in the field of machine learning, and AI has become one of the hottest developments in technology. Many utopian or apocalyptic predictions have emerged about what those advances mean. They have, quite literally, been taken to presage either immortality or the end of the world, and a lot has been written about both these possibilities.

I suspect that developments in AI lead to such strong feelings because of our deep-seated fear of the almost human. The idea that creatures might bridge the gap between the human and the artificial has always been deeply disturbing, from the medieval golem to Frankenstein's monster to Ava, the sexy robot fatale in the movie Ex Machina.

But do computers really learn as well as humans? How much of the heated rhetoric points to revolutionary change, and how much is just hype? The details of how computers learn to recognize, say, a cat, a spoken word or a Japanese character can be hard to follow. But on closer inspection, the basic ideas behind machine learning are not as baffling as they first seem.

One approach tries to solve the problem by starting with the stream of photons and air vibrations that Augie, and all of us, receives—and that reaches the computer as pixels of a digital image and sound samples of an audio recording. It then tries to extract a series of patterns in the digital data that can detect and identify whole objects in the surrounding world. This so-called bottom-up approach has roots in the ideas of philosophers such as David Hume and John Stuart Mill and psychologists such as Ivan Pavlov and B. F. Skinner, among others.

Vocabulary

this way up 天地無用(荷物の向きを指定する上向きの矢印)
▶この記事の読み方
burst 巻き起こること
enthusiasm 熱狂
languish 下火になる
striking 目覚ましい, 著しい
machine learning 機械学習
▶この記事の読み方
apocalyptic 黙示録的な, 終末論的な
literally 文字通り
taken 受け取られる, 受け止められる
presage 予兆する
immortality 不死

suspect ～ではないかと思う
deep-seated 根深い
almost human 人間に極めて近い存在, ほとんど人間
creature (不気味な)生き物, 人造人間
disturbing 心をかき乱す
medieval 中世の
golem ゴーレム
fatale 魔性の

rhetoric 大げさな言葉, レトリック
hype 誇大な宣伝, 大風呂敷
say 例えば
follow たどる, 追跡する
baffling (戸惑うほど)難解な

extract 抽出する
bottom-up ボトムアップ

In the 1980s scientists figured out a compelling and ingenious way to apply bottom-up methods to let computers hunt for meaningful patterns in data. "Connectionist," or "neural network," systems take inspiration from the way that neurons convert light patterns at your retina into representations of the world around you. A neural network does something similar. It uses interconnected processing elements, akin to biological cells, to transform pixels at one layer of the network into increasingly abstract representations—a nose or an entire face—as data are crunched at progressively higher layers.

Neural-network ideas have gone through a recent revival because of new techniques called deep learning—technology now being commercialized by Google, Facebook and other tech giants. The ever increasing power of computers—the exponential increase in computing capability that is captured by what is known as Moore's law—also has a part in the new success of these systems. So does the development of enormously large data sets. With better processing capabilities and more data to crunch, connectionist systems can learn far more effectively than we might have once thought.

Over the years the AI community has seesawed between favoring these kinds of bottom-up solutions to machine learning and alternative top-down approaches. Top-down approaches leverage what a system already knows to help it learn something new. Plato, as well as so-called rationalist philosophers such as René Descartes, believed in a top-down approach to learning—and it played a big role in early AI. In the 2000s such methods also experienced their own rebirth in the form of probabilistic, or Bayesian, modeling.

Like scientists, top-down systems start out by formulating abstract and wide-ranging hypotheses about the world. The systems then make predictions about what the data should look like if those hypotheses are correct. Also like scientists, the systems then revise their hypotheses, depending

Vocabulary

compelling 説得力のある
ingenious 巧妙な
hunt for 探す
connectionist コネクショニズムの
neural network ニューラルネットワーク
▶この記事の読み方
convert 変換する
representation 表現，表象
interconnected 相互接続された
akin to ～に似た
biological cell 生体細胞
abstract 抽象的な
crunch 処理する
progressively 徐々に，段階を追って

go through ～を果たす
deep learning ディープラーニング（深層学習）
commercialize 商業化する
exponential 指数関数的な，急激な
Moore's law ムーアの法則
data set データセット

over the years 長年にわたって
seesaw 一進一退を繰り返す
top-down トップダウン
leverage 活用する
rationalist 合理主義の
probabilistic modelling 確率モデル
Bayesian modeling ベイズモデル
▶この記事の読み方

formulate （仮説を）立てる
wide-ranging 多岐にわたる
hypothesis（複数形**hypotheses**）仮説
revise 修正する

on the outcome of those predictions.

Nigeria, Viagra and Spam

Bottom-up methods are perhaps the most readily understood, so let's consider them first. Imagine that you are trying to get your computer to separate important messages from the spam that arrives in your in-box. You might notice that spam tends to have certain distinguishing characteristics: a long list of recipient addressees, an originating address in Nigeria or Bulgaria, references to $1-million prizes or perhaps mention of Viagra. But perfectly useful messages might look the same. You don't want to miss the announcement that you have earned a promotion or an academic award.

If you compare enough examples of spam against other types of e-mails, you might notice that only the spam tends to have qualities that combine in certain telltale ways—Nigeria, for instance, plus a promise of a $1-million prize together spell trouble. In fact, there might be some quite subtle higher-level patterns that discriminate between the spam messages and the useful ones—misspellings and IP addresses that are not at all obvious, for example. If you could detect them, you could accurately filter out the spam—without fear of missing a notice that your Viagra has shipped.

Bottom-up machine learning can ferret out the relevant clues to solve this kind of task. To do this, a neural network must go through its own learning process. It evaluates millions of examples from huge databases, each labeled as spam or as an authentic e-mail. The computer then extracts a set of identifying features that separate spam from everything else.

In a similar way, the network might inspect Internet images labeled "cat," house," "stegosaurus," and so on. By extracting the common features in each set of images—the pattern that distinguishes all the cats from all the dogs—it can identify new images of a cat, even if it has never seen those particular images before.

Vocabulary

outcome 結果

spam スパム, 迷惑メール
readily 容易に
in-box 受信箱, 受信トレイ
distinguishing 区別のつく, 際立った
recipient 受信者
originating 送信元の
reference 言及
mention 言及
promotion 昇進

telltale それとわかる
spell 意味する
subtle 微妙な
filter out 除外する
miss 見逃す

ferret out 探し出す
relevant 関連した
clue 手がかり
go through 〜を経る, 〜を踏む
authentic 本物の, れっきとした
identifying feature 識別特徴

stegosaurus ステゴサウルス

多くの時間を子どもと過ごしている人なら誰しも，どうして子どもはこうも素早く多くのことを学べるのだろうと疑問に思わずにはいられないだろう。古代ギリシャのプラトン以来，多くの哲学者が同じ疑問に向き合ってきたが，満足のいく答えはいまだに得られていない。私の孫のオージーは5歳になる男の子で，恐竜や宇宙船は言うに及ばず，植物や動物，時計についても知っている。また，他者が望んでいるものや，他者の考え，気持ちがわかる。さらに，そうした知識を使って，見聞きしたものを分類し新たな予測を立てることができる。例えば先日，ニューヨークのアメリカ自然史博物館に展示されているティタノサウルス類の新種について，草食だからそんなに怖くはないよと言い放った。

オージーが環境から受け取っているのは，網膜に次々にぶつかる光子や鼓膜に触れる空気の振動だ。感覚からのこの限定的な情報をもとに，彼の青い目の奥にある神経コンピューターは最終的には植物食恐竜ティタノサウルスに関する推測に到達している。電子コンピューターにも同じことができるのか？　長年の疑問だ。

過去15年ほど，コンピューター科学者と心理学者はその答えを見つけようと努力してきた。子どもは教師や親が与えたほんの少しの情報から多くの知識を得る。しかし，機械知能の飛躍的な進歩にもかかわらず，最強のコンピューターをもってしても5歳児のようにうまくは学習できない。

子どもの脳が実際にどう機能しているかを解明し，それと同じく効率的に機能するデジタル脳を作り上げることは，今後数十年にわたってコンピューター科学者の研究目標となるだろう。その手始めとして，人間の学習に関する私たちの知見の一部を組み込んだ人工知能（AI）の開発が始まっている。

復活

AIの研究は1950年代と1960年代の最初のブームの後，数十年にわたって下火だった。だが，ここ数年間にとりわけ機械学習の分野で著しい進展があり，AIは最新の技術革新の1つになった。AIの進歩が意味することについて，多くのユートピア的あるいはディストピア的な予測がなされている。永遠の命の獲得，または世界の終焉を予兆しているというもので，両方の可能性について多くのことが述べられてきた。

AIの進歩がこのような強い感情を呼び起こすのは，人間に極めて近い存在に対する私たちの根深い恐怖心のためだろう。中世のゴーレムからフランケンシュタインが創造したモンスター，映画『エクス・マキナ』に登場するセクシーな魔性ロボットのエヴァまで，人造人間が人間と人工物のギャップを埋めるかもしれないという考えは常に私たちの心を激しくかき乱してきた。

だが，コンピューターは実際に人間のように上手に学習するのか？　盛んに書き立てられる予測のうちどこまでが画期的な変化を言い当てており，どこからがただの大風呂敷なのか？　コンピューターがどのようにして猫や話し言葉，文字などを認識できるようになったかを詳しく追跡するのは難しいところがある。だがよく考えると，機械学習の背景にある基本的なアイデアはそれほど難解なものではない。

1つのアプローチは，オージーや私たちの誰もが受け取っている光子の流れと空気振動から出発して問題を解決しようとするものだ。光子の流れと空気振動は，それぞれデジタル画像の画素と録音された音声信号としてコンピューターに入力される。コンピューターはそのデジタルデータの中から，周囲にある物体を特定できる一連のパターンを抽出しようと試みる。このボトムアップのアプローチの起源は，ヒューム（David Hume）やミル（John Stuart Mill）などの哲学者と，パブロフ（Ivan Pavlov）やスキナー（B. F. Skinner）などの心理学者の考え方にある。

1980年代，このボトムアップ方式を応用してコンピューターにデータ内の重要なパターンを探させる強力で巧妙な方法が考案された。「コネクショニズム」あるいは「ニューラルネットワーク」と呼ばれるモデルでは，人間の網膜に届いた光のパターンをニューロンがまわりの世界の表現に変換する方法から着想を得ている。ニューラルネットワークはこれと似たことを行う。相互接続された処理ユニット（神経細胞のようなもの）を使って，入力信号の画素を鼻や顔全体といったように段階を追って，より抽象的な表現に変換していく。

ニューラルネットワークの考え方は近年，「ディープラーニング（深層学習）」と呼ばれる新技術のおかげで復活を果たした。現在，この技術はグーグルやフェイスブックなど大手ハイテク企業によって商業化されている。コンピューターの処理能力が向上し続けていること，つまり「ムーアの法則」で語られる計算能力の指数関数的な向上も，ニューラルネットシステムの最近の成功に貢献している。さらに非常に大規模なデータセットの開発もこれに寄与している。処理能力の向上とデータ量の増加のおかげで，ニューラルネットシステムはかつて考えられていたよりもはるかに効率的に学習できるようになった。

AI界は長年，機械学習の方法としてこうしたボトムアップ方式を採用したりトップダウン方式を採用したりを繰り返してきた。トップダウンのアプロー

この記事の読み方

いま社会や世界を大きく変えつつある人工知能（AI）。だが，その研究開発は必ずしも順調に進んできたわけではない。1960 年代末からは停滞の時期が長く続いた。ブレイクスルーになったのは，machine learning（機械学習）にボトムアップとトップダウンの 2 つの方式を採用したことだった。具体的には，前者は deep learning（ディープラーニング／深層学習），後者は Bayesian modeling（ベイズモデル）に相当する。本記事では，子どもが学習の際に採用しているのがこの 2 つの方式であり，子どもの認知についての研究成果が AI の復活に貢献したことが述べられている。

小見出しの “This Way Up”（天地無用）は，向きの異なるこの 2 つのアプローチに絡めた表現。訳文は，本文の内容に則して「復活」にしてある。

neural network はニューラルネットワーク，神経ネットワーク，神経回路網と訳せるが，どれにするかは好みの問題（次の記事では神経回路網と訳してある）。ただ，カタカナ表記か漢字表記かは統一したほうがよい（ニューラルネットワークならディープラーニング，神経回路網なら深層学習というように）。

記事の原題は “Making AI More Human”（AI をより人間らしくする）。邦題は，子どもの認知研究の知見の応用という点を前面に出したものにしてある。

チでは，システムは既有の知識を活用して新しいことを学習する。プラトンも，デカルト（René Descartes）などのいわゆる合理主義の哲学者も，学習にはトップダウンのアプローチが重要だと信じていた。このアプローチは初期 AI で大きな役割を果たし，2000 年代に入ると「確率モデル」あるいは「ベイズモデル」という形で復活を果たした。

トップダウンのシステムはまず，科学者がするように世界についての抽象的で多岐にわたる仮説を立てる。次に，その仮説が正しい場合にデータがどのようなものになるかを予測する。そして，やはり科学者のように，予測結果をもとに自らの仮説を修正する。

ボトムアップのアプローチ

ボトムアップ方式のほうが理解しやすいと思われるので，まずはこちらから説明しよう。コンピューターに受信メールから迷惑メールを選別させることを考えよう。迷惑メールには往々にして際立った特徴があることはご存じだろう。受信者リストが長いことや，送信元がナイジェリアやブルガリアであること，本文に「100 万ドルの賞金」や「バイアグラ」といった語句が含まれていることなどだ。だが，正規のメールも同じように見える場合があるかもしれない。昇進や学術賞の授与を知らせるメールを見落としたくはない。

十分な数の迷惑メールと正規メールを比べれば，迷惑メールにはそれとわかる形で複数の特徴が含まれていることに気づく。例えば送信元がナイジェリアで，かつ本文に「100 万ドルの賞金」が含まれているのは迷惑メールだ。実際には，スペルミスや送信元がまったく不明な IP アドレスなど，迷惑メールと正規のメールを区別するかなり微妙でより高度なパターンが存在するだろう。それらを検出できれば，迷惑メールを正確に除外できる（実際にネット注文したバイアグラが発送されたという知らせを見逃す心配なしに）。

ボトムアップ方式の機械学習は，関連する手がかりを探し出してこの種の課題を解決する。そのために，ニューラルネットワークは学習過程を踏まねばならない。「迷惑メール」あるいは「正規メール」とラベル付けされた何百万通ものメールを巨大データベースから読み込み，迷惑メールを選り分ける一連の特徴を抽出するのだ。

同様に，「猫」や「家」，「ステゴサウルス」などとラベル付けされたネット上の画像を調べてもよい。それぞれの画像セットに共通する特徴（すべての犬画像とすべての猫画像を区別するパターンなど）を抽出することで，ニューラルネットワークは新たに提示された猫の画像を，たとえ初めて見るものであっても，猫と認識できる。

Alison Gopnik
米カリフォルニア大学バークレー校の心理学教授で哲学の教授を兼任。幼児がどのように世界を知るかを研究テーマとしている。

How Matter Becomes Mind

神経回路網は
どのように知性を
生み出すのか

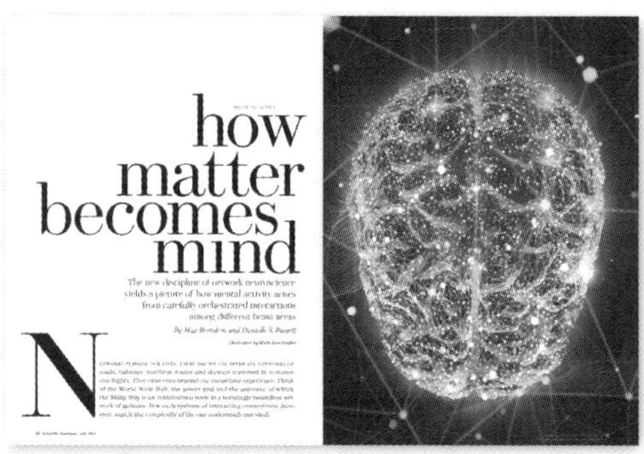

M. ベルトレロ／ D. S. バセット
（ともに米ペンシルベニア大学）

「ネットワーク神経科学」という新分野の研究によって
異なる脳領域間の入念に調整された相互作用から
精神活動が立ち上がってくる仕組みが見えてきた

KEY CONCEPTS

脳は複数の領域が協働するネットワーク

■脳から知性がどのように生まれるのか？　この疑問から生まれた新たな学問分野「ネットワーク神経科学」では，読み書きや計算，あるいは単に座って指先で机を軽くたたくといった行動を可能にしている脳領域間の結びつきを，グラフ理論という数学の手法を使ってモデル化する。

■グラフ理論は，視覚や注意，自制などの認知能力を生み出す機能的ネットワークを形作っている物理的な神経経路をモデル化する。

■個別のニューロンや脳領域を超えて脳をネットワークとしてとらえることで，物質と精神の間の隔たりをつなぐ。うつ病などの精神疾患を診断・治療する新手法の開発など，実用的な恩恵も期待できそうだ。

日経サイエンス 2020 年 3 月号，SCIENTIFIC AMERICAN July 2019

Networks pervade our lives. Every day we use intricate networks of roads, railways, maritime routes and skyways traversed by commercial flights. They exist even beyond our immediate experience. Think of the World Wide Web, the power grid and the universe, of which the Milky Way is an infinitesimal node in a seemingly boundless network of galaxies. Few such systems of interacting connections, however, match the complexity of the one underneath our skull.

Neuroscience has gained a higher profile in recent years, as many people have grown familiar with splashily colored images that show brain regions "lighting up" during a mental task. There is, for instance, the temporal lobe, the area by your ear, which is involved with memory, and the occipital lobe at the back of your head, which dedicates itself to vision.

What has been missing from this account of human brain function is how all these distinct regions interact to give rise to who we are. Our laboratory and others have borrowed a language from a branch of mathematics called graph theory that allows us to parse, probe and predict complex interactions of the brain that bridge the seemingly vast gap between frenzied neural electrical activity and an array of cognitive tasks—sensing, remembering, making decisions, learning a new skill and initiating movement. This new field of network neuroscience builds on and reinforces the idea that certain regions of the brain carry out defined activities. In the most fundamental sense, what the brain is—and thus who we are as conscious beings—is, in fact, defined by a sprawling network of 100 billion neurons with at least 100 trillion connecting points, or synapses.

Network neuroscience seeks to capture this complexity. We can now model the data supplied by brain imaging as a graph composed of nodes and edges. In a graph,

Vocabulary

［タイトル］ **matter** 物質
▶この記事の読み方

pervade 浸透する
intricate 入り組んだ，複雑な
maritime route 海上航路
skyway 航空路
traverse 行き交う，飛び交う
immediate experience 直接経験
power grid 電力網
Milky Way 天の川銀河
infinitesimal 微小な
node ノード（節点）
seemingly boundless 無限とも思える
interacting 相互作用する
match 匹敵する
gain a higher profile ますます世間の注目を集める
splashily colored 色鮮やかな
mental task 知的作業，認知課題
temporal lobe 側頭葉
involved with ～に関わる
occipital lobe 後頭葉
vision 視覚
missing 抜け落ちている
distinct 異なる
give rise to ～を生じさせる
borrow 借りる
graph theory グラフ理論
parse 読み解く
probe 探る
seemingly 一見
frenzied 興奮した
neural electrical activity 神経の電気活動
an array of たくさんの，一連の
cognitive task 認知課題
initiate 開始する，起こす
network neuroscience ネットワーク神経科学
▶この記事の読み方
build on ～に基づく
defined 定められた，決まった
sprawling 広範囲に広がった
synapse シナプス

nodes represent the units of the network, such as neurons or, in another context, airports. Edges serve as the connections between nodes—think of one neuron intertwined to the next or contemplate airline flight routes. In our work, the human brain is reduced to a graph of roughly 300 nodes. Diverse areas can be linked together by edges representing the brain's structural connections: thick bundles of tubular wires called white matter tracts that tie together brain regions. This depiction of the brain as a unified network has already furnished a clearer picture of cognitive functioning, along with the practical benefit of enabling better diagnoses and treatment of psychiatric disorders. As we glimpse ahead, an understanding of brain networks may lead to a blueprint for improved artificial intelligence, new medicines and electrical-stimulation technology to alter malfunctioning neural circuitry in depression—and perhaps also the development of genetic therapies to treat mental illness.

Vocabulary

edge エッジ（辺）
represent 表す
unit 構成単位
intertwine 結び付ける
contemplate 考える
reduce 還元する
diverse 多様な
bundle 束
tubular 管状の
white matter tract 白質路
depiction 描写
furnish 提供する
diagnosis（複 **diagnoses**）診断
psychiatric disorder 精神疾患
glimpse ちらりと見る
ahead あらかじめ
artificial intelligence 人工知能
electrical stimulation 電気刺激
neural circuitry 神経回路
depression うつ病, うつ状態
genetic therapy 遺伝子治療
mental illness 精神疾患

The Music of the Mind

To understand how networks underlie our cognitive capabilities, first consider the analogy of an orchestra playing a symphony. Until recently, neuroscientists have largely studied the functioning of individual brain regions in isolation, the neural equivalent of separate brass, percussion, strings and woodwind sections. In the brain, this stratification represents an approach that dates back to Plato—quite simply, it entails carving nature at the joints and then studying the individual components that remain.

underlie ～の根底にある
cognitive capability 認知能力
analogy なぞらえること
in isolation 切り離して
stratification 層化, 階層化
Plato プラトン
quite simply 簡単に言えば, 要するに
entail 含意する, 意味する
carve 切り分ける
joint つなぎ目

Just as it is useful to understand how the amygdala helps to process emotions, it is similarly vital to grasp how a violin produces high-pitched sounds. Still, even a complete list of brain regions and their functions—vision, motor, emotion, and so on—does not tell us how the brain really works. Nor does an inventory of instruments provide a recipe for Beethoven's Eroica symphony.

amygdala 扁桃体
emotion 情動
motor 運動
inventory 一覧表, 目録

Network neuroscientists have begun to tame these mysteries by examining the way each brain region is embedded in a larger network of such regions and by mapping the connections between regions to study how each is embedded in the large, integrated network that is the brain. There are two major approaches. First, examining structural connectivity captures the instrumentation of the brain's orchestra. It is the physical means of creating the music, and the unique instrumentation of a given musical work constrains what can be played. Instrumentation matters, but it is not the music itself. Put another way, just as a collection of instruments is not music, an assemblage of wires does not represent brain function.

Vocabulary

tame 克服する, 手なずける
embed 埋め込む
integrated 統合された
structural connectivity 構造的なつながり
capture 把握する
instrumentation 楽器編成
constrain 制限する
matter 重要である
put another way 別の言い方をすると
assemblage 集まり

Second, living brains are massive orchestras of neurons that fire together in quite specific patterns. We hear a brain's music by measuring the correlation between the activity of each pair of regions, indicating that they are working in concert. This measure of joint activity is known as functional connectivity, and we colloquially think of it as reflecting the music of the brain. If two regions fire with the same time-varying fluctuations, they are considered to be functionally connected. This music is just as important as the decibels produced by a French horn or viola. The volume of the brain's music can be thought of as the level of activity of electrical signals buzzing about one brain area or another.

fire 発火する
correlation 相関
in concert 協調して
functional connectivity 機能的結びつき
colloquially 口語表現で
time-varying 時間とともに変化する
fluctuation 変動, 揺らぎ
decibel 音量
buzz about 飛び交う

At any moment, though, some areas within the three-pound organ are more active than others. We have all heard the saying that people use a small fraction of their brain capacity. In fact, the entire brain is active at any point in time, but a given task modulates the activity of only a portion of the brain from its baseline level of activity.

at any moment いつでも
fraction 一部
modulate 調節する

That arrangement does not mean that you fulfill only half of your cognitive potential. In fact, if your entire brain were strongly active at the same time, it would be

arrangement 体制
cognitive potential 認知能力

as if all the orchestra members were playing as loudly as possible—and that scenario would create chaos, not enable communication. The deafening sound would not convey the emotional overtones present in a great musical piece. It is the pitch, rhythms, tempo and strategic pauses that communicate information, both during a symphony and inside your head.

Vocabulary

deafening 耳をつんざくような
overtone 響き
pitch 音高
pause 休止，間（ま）

Modularity

Just as an orchestra can be divided into groups of instruments from different families, the brain can be separated into collections of nodes called modules—a description of localized networks. All brains are modular. Even the 302-neuron network of the nematode *Caenorhabditis elegans* has a modular structure. Nodes within a module share stronger connections to one another than to nodes in other modules.

modularity モジュール方式
module モジュール
description 呼称
localized network 局所的なネットワーク
nematode 線虫
Caenorhabditis elegans 線虫の学名

Each module in the brain has a certain function, just as every family of instruments plays a role in the symphony. We recently performed an evaluation of a large number of independent studies—a meta-analysis—that included more than 10,000 functional magnetic resonance imaging (fMRI) experiments of subjects performing 83 different cognitive tasks and discovered that separate tasks map to different brain-network modules. There are modules occupied with attention, memory and introspective thought. Other modules, we found, are dedicated to hearing, motor movement and vision.

meta-analysis メタ解析
magnetic resonance imaging 磁気共鳴画像法
subject 被験者
map to ～に割り当てられる
attention 注意
memory 記憶
introspective thought 内省的思考
hearing 聴覚
motor movement 運動

These sensory and motor cognitive processes involve single, contiguous modules, most of which are confined to one lobe of the brain. We also found that computations in modules do not spur more activity in other modules—a critical aspect of modular processing. Imagine a scenario in which every musician in an orchestra had to change the notes played every time another musician changed his or her notes. The orchestra would spiral out

sensory 感覚の
contiguous 隣接する
confined to ～に限定される
lobe 葉（よう）
computation 計算，情報処理
spur 拍車をかける，刺激する
critical 極めて重要な，決定的な
note 音
spiral out of control 手に負えない状況に陥る

of control and would certainly not produce aesthetically pleasing sounds. Processing in the brain is similar—each module must be able to function mostly independently. Philosophers as early as Plato and as recent as Jerry Fodor have noted this necessity, and our research confirms it.

Even though brain modules are largely independent, a symphony requires that families of instruments be played in unison. Information generated by one module must eventually be integrated with other modules. Watching a movie with only a brain module for vision—without access to the one for emotions—would detract greatly from the experience.

For that reason, to complete many cognitive tasks, modules must often work together. A short-term memory task—holding a new phone number in your head—requires the cooperation of auditory, attention and memory-processing modules. To integrate and control the activity of multiple modules, the brain uses hubs—nodes where connections from the brain's different modules meet.

Vocabulary

aesthetically pleasing 美的に快い

in unison ユニゾン（斉奏）で，調和して
eventually 最終的に
detract 損ねる，興をそぐ

short-term memory 短期記憶
auditory 聴覚の
hub ハブ

ネットワークは人間生活のあらゆる場に存在している。私たちは毎日，道路網や鉄道網，海路，民間機が飛び交う航空路などの複雑なネットワークを利用している。さらにネットワークは直接経験を超えたところにも存在している。ワールドワイドウェブや電力網，宇宙もネットワークだ。天の川銀河は，無限とも思える広大な銀河のネットワークの中ではほんの小さな1つの点にすぎない。だが，互いに影響し合う点の集まりからなるこうしたシステムの中でも，人間の頭蓋骨の中にあるシステムほど複雑なものはないといえる。

近年，神経科学はますます世間の注目を集めている。活動中の脳領域が明るく“輝いて”見える色鮮やかな脳画像は多くの人にお馴染みになった。そうした画像から，耳の近くにある脳の側頭葉は記憶に関わり，頭の後ろ側にある後頭葉は視覚に関与しているといったことがわかる。

ただ，こうした脳機能の説明には，これらの異なる脳領域がどのように相互作用して私たちの意識が生じるのかという点が抜け落ちている。そこで私たちを含むいくつかの研究室は「グラフ理論」という数学分野の手法を活用し，脳内の複雑な相互作用を読み解き，検出し，予測しようとしている。脳神経の電気活動と一連の認知課題（知覚や記憶，意思決定，新たな技能の学習，体を動かすなど）の間にある巨大な隔たりをつなぐ試みだ。「ネットワーク神経科学」と呼ばれるこの新分野は，脳の特定領域が決まった活動を担っているという考えに基づいており，その考えを強化するものでもある。脳とは何か，つまり意識を持つ人間とは何なのかは，突き詰めれば1000億個のニューロンが100兆カ所を超える接点（シナプス）でつながった広大なネットワークによって決まっている。

ネットワーク神経科学は脳のこの複雑さをとらえるため，脳画像から得られたデータをノード（節点）とエッジ（辺）で構成されるグラフとしてモデル化する。ノードはニューロンや空港など，ネットワークの構成単位を表す。エッジはノード間のつながりを表し，例えばニューロンどうしの接続や飛行機の航路が該当する。私たちの研究では，人間の脳を約300個のノードからなるグラフに還元する。脳のさまざまな領域が，構造的な接続を表すエッジで結びついている。つまり，神経線維の太い束である「白質路」が各脳領域を結んでいるのだ。このように統合されたネットワークとして脳をとらえることで，認知機能をより明確に把握できるようになったほか，精神疾患の的確な診断・治療が可能になっている。後述するように，脳のネットワークの理解はより優れた人工知能（AI）や，うつ病で機能不全に陥っている神経回路を治す新薬や電気刺激法の設計につながる可能性がある。さらには精神疾患の遺伝子治療を可能にするかもしれない。

脳が紡ぐ音楽

私たちの認知能力がネットワークからどのように生まれるのかを理解するために，脳を交響曲を演奏するオーケストラになぞらえてみよう。神経科学者は最近まで，主に脳の各領域を個別に調べてきた。オーケストラを弦楽器と木管，金管，打楽器の各セクションに分けて考えるようなものだ。こうした分け方はプラトンの時代にまでさかのぼる考え方で，自然の現象をつなぎ目のところで切り

この記事の読み方

記事の原題は “How Matter Becomes Mind”（どのようにして物質から心が生まれるのか）。ここで物質と言っているのは脳のこと，具体的には神経回路網。邦題はそれがわかる形にしてある。

脳全体の神経間のつながりは connectome（コネクトーム）と呼ばれる。これをあつかうのが network neuroscience（ネットワーク神経科学）。記事では，グラフ理論を用いて，nodes（ノード／節点）と edges（エッジ／辺）によってつながりを視覚化するアプローチが紹介されている。

独立してひとつの機能をはたすノード群（いわば機能単位）は，modules（モジュール）と呼ばれる。記事では，これらのモジュールが協同ではたらくことによって，認知（あるいは知性や心）が生み出されることが解説されている。図が添えられていないため，文章だけから内容をイメージするのは難しいかもしれない。

記事の後半では，認知課題（全部で 83 種類）遂行中の脳活動を計測したいくつもの研究の結果をメタ解析し，それぞれの認知課題に各モジュールがどう関わっているかを論じている。カラー見開き 2 ページで示されている脳のネットワークは，さながら宇宙に散らばる銀河のようだ。

分けて，個々の構成要素を調べる。

扁桃体が情動をどう処理しているかを理解することが役立つのと同じように，バイオリンがどのようにして高音を発するのかを理解することは重要だ。だが，脳の各領域とその機能（視覚や運動，情動など）の完全な対応表を手に入れたとしても，脳が実際にどう働いているのかはわからない。楽器の目録があったからといって，ベートーベンの交響曲「英雄」の演奏にはならないのと同じだ。

ネットワーク神経科学者は個別の脳領域がどのように結びついて領域間ネットワークを形作っているかを調べ，脳という大きな統合ネットワークの中にどう埋め込まれているかをマッピングすることで，脳の働きに迫ろうとしている。主なアプローチは２つある。１つは，脳の構造的なつながりを調べて，脳というオーケストラの楽器編成を把握することだ。楽器編成は音楽を演奏するための物理的な手段であり，それぞれの音楽作品が採用する楽器編成によって，何が演奏できるかが制限される。ただ，楽器編成は重要だが，音楽そのものではない。別の言い方をすると，楽器の集まりが音楽ではないのと同様，配線の集まりは脳の機能を表してはいない。

２つ目は，脳は極めて特徴的なパターンで同時に発火するニューロン群からなる大規模なオーケストラであることに注目する。脳が奏でる音楽は，２つの脳領域の活動の相関を測定することによって聴くことができる。２つの脳領域がどれだけ協調して働いているかを示すこの指標は「機能的結びつき」と呼ばれ，脳の音楽を反映していると考えてよいだろう。２つの脳領域の神経活動が同じ時間的変動を示している場合，両者は機能的につながっていると考えられる。オーケストラでホルンやビオラなど個別の楽器群が出す音量が重要であるように，脳の音楽でも音量が重要だ。脳の各領域で発生し領域間を飛び交っている電気信号の活動レベルが，この音量だと考えることができる。

だが，脳の活動には領域間で常に強弱の差がある。「人は脳の力のごく一部しか使っていない」とよく言われる。実際，脳全体は絶えず活動しているのだが，ある課題を受けて活動レベルがベースラインから変わるのは脳のほんの一部だけだ。

これは脳の認知能力の半分しか使っていないという意味ではない。それどころか脳全体が一斉に強く活動すれば，オーケストラの全楽員が最大の音量で演奏しているようなもので，大混乱に陥ってコミュニケーション不能となるだろう。耳をつんざく音は，偉大な音楽作品に込められた感情的な響きを伝えはしない。交響曲も脳の音楽も，情報を伝えるのは音のピッチとリズム，テンポ，意図的な間なのだ。

モジュール方式

オーケストラを異なる種類の楽器のパートに分割できるように，脳も「モジュール」というノードの集合（つまり局所的なネットワーク）に分けることができる。あらゆる生物の脳がモジュール方式になっている。たった302個のニューロンからなる線虫の神経ネットワークでさえモジュール構造だ。同じモジュール中のノードどうしの結びつきは，他のモジュールのノードとの結びつきよりも強い。

交響曲の演奏で各楽器パートがそれぞれの役割を果たすのと同様に，脳の各モジュールは特定の機能を持っている。私たちは最近，多数の独立した研究結果をまとめて評価するメタ解析を行った。合計83種類の認知課題を実行している際の脳活動を機能的磁気共鳴画像装置（fMRI）で撮影した1万件を超える画像から，異なる課題はそれぞれ異なるモジュールに割り当てられることがわかった。注意や記憶，内省的思考を担うモジュールもあれば，聴覚や運動，視覚に特化したモジュールもある。

これら感覚や運動の認知過程には単一の隣接したモジュール群が関与しており，その大部分は1つの脳葉内に存在している。また，あるモジュールにおける情報処理が他のモジュールを活性化することはないこともわかった。これはモジュール方式の決定的な特徴だ。オーケストラの全員が，他の楽員が奏でる音を変えるたびに自分の音も変えなければならないとしたらどうだろう。オーケストラは制御不能に陥り，美しく快い演奏は決して生まれないだろう。脳の情報処理も同様で，各モジュールはほぼ独立して機能できなければならない。古代ギリシャのプラトンから現代のフォーダー（Jerry Fodor）に至る哲学者がモジュールの必要性を指摘しており，私たちの研究はそれを確認した。

脳のモジュールはほぼ独立しているが，交響曲ではさまざまな楽器群を協調させて演奏する必要がある。同じように，あるモジュールが生み出した情報は最終的に他のモジュールと統合されなければならない。脳の視覚モジュールだけを使って映画を見て，感情モジュールへのアクセスがなかったら，鑑賞の楽しさはひどく損なわれるだろう。

このため，多くの認知課題を完遂するにはモジュールどうしの協調が必要になる。例えば短期記憶の課題（新たな電話番号を覚えておくなど）では聴覚と注意，記憶処理の各モジュールの連携が必要だ。そして複数のモジュールの活動を統合・制御するため，脳は「ハブ」を用いる。異なるモジュールからの接続が集まるノードがハブだ。

Max Bertolero／Danielle S. Bassett
バセットは米ペンシルベニア大学生物工学科の准教授で，物理系と生物系のネットワークを研究している。2014年にマッカーサー・フェローになった。ベルトレロはバセットが率いる複雑系グループのポスドク研究員。米カリフォルニア大学バークレー校でシステム神経科学の博士号を，米コロンビア大学で哲学および心理学の学士号を取得。

創造する心

4

Infectious Dreams

パンデミックが変えた睡眠と夢

Nap Like a Genius

天才のようにまどろめ　エジソンに学ぶ半覚醒状態のひらめき

The Science of Genius

創造性の起源

Infectious Dreams

パンデミックが変えた睡眠と夢

T. ニールセン
(加モントリオール大学)

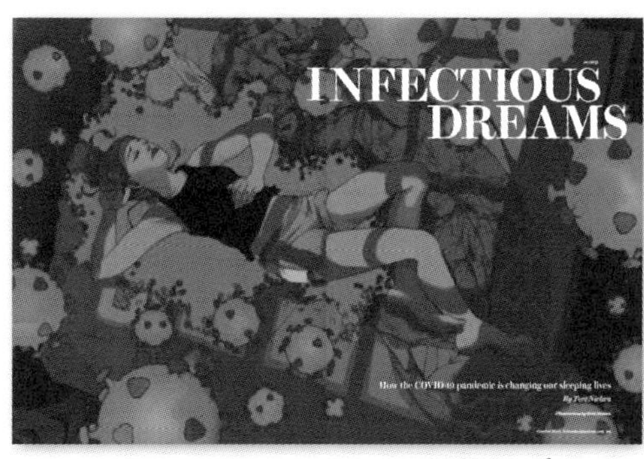

COVID-19のパンデミックによって生活が激変した結果
人々はより遅くまで眠るようになり，悪夢を見ることが多くなった

KEY CONCEPTS

夢に備わった意外な機能

■COVID-19のパンデミックによる生活の激変で，人々はより長く，より遅くまで眠るようになり，夢を想起することや悪夢を見ることが増えた。

■夢には問題解決を助ける，恐怖の記憶を消去する，社会的状況をシミュレーションするなど，非常に幅広い機能がある。

■パンデミックによって人類の夢に恒久的な変化が起きる可能性があるが，ポストコロナ時代における長期的な適応にどう影響するかは未知数だ。

日経サイエンス 2020 年 12 月号，SCIENTIFIC AMERICAN October 2020

For many of us, living in a COVID-19 world feels as if we have been thrown into an alternative reality. We live day and night inside the same walls. We fear touching groceries that arrive at our doorstep. If we venture into town we wear masks, and we get anxious if we pass someone who is not. We have trouble discerning faces. It's like living in a dream.

COVID-19 has altered our dream worlds, too: how much we dream, how many of our dreams we remember and the nature of our dreams themselves. Early this year, when stay-at-home directives were put in place widely, society quite unexpectedly experienced what I am calling a dream surge: a global increase in the reporting of vivid, bizarre dreams, many of which are concerned with coronavirus and social distancing. Terms such as coronavirus dreams, lockdown dreams and COVID nightmares emerged on social media. By early April, social and mainstream media outlets had begun broadcasting the message: the world is dreaming about COVID-19.

Although widespread changes in dreaming had been reported in the U.S. following extraordinary events such as the 9/11 attacks in 2001 and the 1989 San Francisco earthquake, a surge of this magnitude had never been documented. This upwelling of dreams is the first to occur globally and the first to happen in the era of social media, which makes dreams readily accessible for immediate study. As a dream "event," the pandemic is unprecedented.

But what kind of phenomenon is this, exactly? Why was it happening with such vigor? To find out, Deirdre Barrett, an assistant professor at Harvard University and editor in chief of the journal Dreaming, initiated a COVID-19 dreams survey online in the week of March 22. Erin and Grace Gravley, San Francisco Bay Area artists, launched IDreamofCovid.com, a site archiving and illustrating pandemic dreams. The Twitter account @Covid-

Vocabulary

［タイトル］ **infectious** 感染性の

alternative 別の
grocery 食料品
venture into 思い切って～する
pass すれ違う，～のそばを通る
discern 見分ける

alter 変える
stay-at-home directive 外出禁止令
dream surge ドリームサージ（夢の急増）
▶この記事の読み方
bizarre 奇妙な
nightmare 悪夢
outlet 発信元

upwelling 高まり
readily すぐに
unprecedented 未曾有の

vigor 力強さ
initiate 開始する

Dreams began operation. Kelly Bulkeley, a psychologist of religion and director of the Sleep and Dream Database, followed with a YouGov survey of 2,477 American adults. And my former doctoral student Elizaveta Solomonova, now a postdoctoral fellow at McGill University, along with Rebecca Robillard of the Royal's Institute of Mental Health Research in Ottawa and others, launched a survey to which 968 people aged 12 and older responded, almost all in North America. Results of these inquiries, not yet published in journals but available in preliminary form online, document the precipitous surge, the striking variety of dreams and many related mental health effects.

Vocabulary

religion 宗教
doctoral 博士課程の
postdoctoral ポスドク(博士課程修了後)の
inquiry 調査
precipitous 急激な
striking 著しい, 驚くべき

Bulkeley's three-day poll revealed that in March, 29 percent of Americans recalled more dreams than usual. Solomonova and Robillard found that 37 percent of people had pandemic dreams, many marked by themes of insufficiently completing tasks (such as losing control of a vehicle) and being threatened by others. Many online posts reflect these findings. One person, whose Twitter handle is @monicaluhar, reported, "Had a dream about returning as a sub teacher in the fall, unprepared. Students were having a difficult time practicing social distancing, and teachers couldn't stagger classes or have one-on-one meetings." And @therealbeecarey said, "My phone had a virus and was posting so many random pictures from my camera roll to instagram and my anxiety was at an all time high."

poll 世論調査
recall 思い出す, 想起する
threaten 脅す
sub teacher 補助教員
stagger 時差制にする

More recent studies found qualitative changes in dream emotions and concerns about health. Dream reports from Brazilian adults in social isolation had high proportions of words related to anger, sadness, contamination and cleanliness. Text mining of accounts of 810 Finnish dreams showed that most word clusters were laden with anxiousness; 55 percent were about the pandemic directly (lack of regard for social distancing, elderly people in trouble), and these emotions were more prevalent among people who felt increased stress during the day. A study

qualitative 質的な
social isolation 社会的隔離
contamination 汚染
text mining テキストマイニング
word cluster 単語クラスター
laden with ～でいっぱいの
in trouble 苦境に陥って
prevalent 広まっている

of 100 nurses conscripted to treat COVID-19 patients in Wuhan, China, revealed that 45 percent experienced nightmares—twice the lifetime rate among Chinese psychiatric outpatients and many times higher than that among the 5 percent of the general population who have nightmare disorder.

It seems clear that some basic biological and social dynamics may have played a role in this unprecedented opening of the oneiric floodgates. At least three factors may have triggered or sustained the dream surge: disrupted sleep schedules augmenting the amount of REM sleep and therefore dreaming; threats of contagion and social distancing taxing dreaming's capacity to regulate emotions; and social and mainstream media amplifying the public's reaction to the surge.

More REM Sleep, More Dreams

One obvious explanation for the surge is that sleep patterns changed abruptly when lockdowns took effect. Early publications demonstrate elevated levels of insomnia in the Chinese population, especially among front-line workers. In contrast, stay-at-home orders, which removed long commutes to work, improved sleep for many people. Chinese respondents reported an average increase of 46 minutes in bed and an extra 34 minutes in total sleep time. Some 54 percent of people in Finland said they slept more after lockdown. Overall, from March 13 to 27, time asleep in the U.S. increased almost 20 percent nationwide, and states with the longest commute times, such as Maryland and New Jersey, showed the largest increases.

Longer slumber leads to more dreams; people in sleep laboratories who are allowed to snooze more than 9.5 hours recall more dreams than when sleeping a typical eight hours. Sleeping longer also proportionally increases rapid eye movement (REM) sleep, which is when the most vivid and emotional dreams occur.

Vocabulary

conscript 徴集する, 招集する
psychiatric 精神科の
outpatient 外来患者
nightmare disorder 悪夢障害

dynamics （影響を与える）力, 力学
oneiric 夢の
floodgate 水門
trigger 引き金となる
disrupted 混乱した, 妨げられた
augment 増やす
REM sleep レム睡眠
threat 脅威
contagion 感染
tax 負担をかける
amplify 増幅させる

abruptly 突然（に）
take effect 実施される
elevated 高い
insomnia 不眠症
front-line 第一線の, 最前線の
commute 通勤
respondent 回答者
overall 総じて

slumber 眠り
snooze 居眠りする, 眠る
proportionally 比例して

Relaxed schedules may also have caused dreaming to occur later than usual in the morning, when REM sleep is more prevalent and intense and, thus, dreams are more bizarre. Dream-tweets reflect these qualities: "I was taking care of a newborn girl that had COVID ... it was so vivid and real." Increased dreaming during late-morning REM intervals results from the convergence of several processes. Sleep itself cycles through deep and light stages about every 90 minutes, but pressure for REM sleep gradually increases as the need for deep, recuperative sleep is progressively satisfied. Meanwhile a circadian process that is tightly linked to our 24-hour core body temperature rhythm gives an abrupt boost to REM sleep propensity late in the sleep period and stays elevated through the morning.

Vocabulary

relaxed ゆとりのある
result from ～に起因する
convergence 収束
cycle through ～を周期的に繰り返す
recuperative 回復につながる
circadian 24時間周期の
core body temperature 深部体温
propensity 傾向
rapid eye movement 急速眼球運動

After the pandemic began, many people did sleep longer and later. In China, average weekly bedtime was delayed by 26 minutes but wake-up time by 72 minutes. These values were 41 and 73 minutes in Italy and 30 and 42 minutes among U.S. university students. And without commutes, many people were freer to linger in bed, remembering their dreams. Some early birds may have turned into night owls, who typically have more REM sleep and more frequent nightmares. And as people eliminated whatever sleep debts they may have accrued over days or even weeks of insufficient rest, they were more likely to wake up at night and remember more dreams.

linger ぐずぐずする
early bird 早起きの人
night owl 夜更かしをする人
sleep debt 睡眠負債
accrue 蓄積する

Dream Functions Overwhelmed

The subject matter of many COVID-19 dreams directly or metaphorically reflects fears about contagion and the challenges of social distancing. Even in normal times, we dream more about novel experiences. For example, people enrolled in programs to rapidly learn French dream more about French. Replaying fragments of experiences is one example of a functional role that researchers widely ascribe to REM sleep and dreaming: it helps us solve problems. Other roles include consolidating the prior day's

overwhelm 圧倒する
subject matter 主題
metaphorically 隠喩的に
normal times 平時, 普段
novel 新奇な, 新しい
enroll 登録する
replay 再生する
fragment 断片
ascribe to ～のものと見なす
consolidate 定着させる

events into longer-lasting memories, fitting those events into an ongoing narrative of our lives and helping us regulate emotions.

Researchers have documented countless cases of dreams assisting in creative achievement. Empirical studies also show that REM sleep aids in problem-solving that requires access to wide-ranging memory associations, which may explain why so many dreams in the 2020 surge involve creative or strange attempts to deal with a COVID-19 problem. One survey respondent said, "I was looking for a kind of cream that would either prevent or cure Covid-19. I got my hands on the last bottle."

Two other widely claimed dream functions are extinguishing fearful memories and simulating social situations. They are related to emotion regulation and help to explain why pandemic threats and social distancing challenges appear so often in surge dreams. Many dreams reported in the media include fearful reactions to infection, finances and social distancing. "I tested positive for pregnancy and covid ... now I'm stressed." Threats may take the form of metaphoric imagery such as tsunamis or aliens; zombies are common. Images of insects, spiders and other small creatures are also widely represented: "My foot was covered in ants and 5-6 black widows were imbedded in the bottom of my foot."

One way to understand direct and metaphoric imagery is to consider that dreams express an individual's core concerns, drawing on memories that are similar in emotional tone but different in subject matter. This contextualization is clear in post-traumatic nightmares, in which a person's reaction to a trauma, such as terror during an assault, is depicted as terror in the face of a natural disaster such as a tsunami. The late Ernest Hartmann, a Boston-area dream and nightmare research pioneer who studied dreams after the 9/11 attacks, stipulated that such contex-

Vocabulary

narrative 物語
regulate 制御する，調節する

creative achievement 創造的な仕事の実現
empirical study 実証研究
problem-solving 問題解決
memory association 連合記憶

extinguish 消す
infection 感染
positive 陽性
pregnancy 妊娠
insect 昆虫
black widow クロゴケグモ（毒グモ）
imbedded 埋め込まれて，入り込んで

draw on 利用する
contextualization 文脈化
posttraumatic 外傷後の
terror 恐怖
assault 暴行，攻撃
depict 描く
late 故（故人）
stipulate 規定する

tualization best helps people adapt when it weaves together old and new experiences. Successful integration produces a more stable memory system that is resilient to future traumas.

Vocabulary

adapt 適応する
weave together 撚り合わせる，編む
integration 統合
resilient 回復力を持つ

コロナ下の生活は，別の世界に放り込まれたかのようだ。多くの人がそう感じている。昼も夜も同じ部屋で過ごし，宅配で届いた食料品に触ることにも不安を感じる。思い切って町に出るときはマスクをつけ，マスクをしない人のそばを通ると心配になる。人の顔を見分けるのも大変だ。それは，まるで夢の中で生きているようである。

COVID-19は，私たちの夢の世界をも変えた。どれくらい夢を見てどのくらい覚えているか，そして夢そのものの性質も変化した。2020年前半に広い範囲で外出が禁止されると，意外にも，私が「ドリームサージ（夢の急増）」と呼んでいる現象が起きた。鮮明かつ奇妙な夢を見たという報告が世界中で増加し，その多くはコロナウイルスやソーシャルディスタンシングに関するものだった。SNSには「コロナウイルスの夢」「ロックダウンの夢」「COVIDの悪夢」などの言葉が現れた。2020年4月上旬にはソーシャルメディアやマスコミがこう報じ始めた。「世界はCOVID-19の夢を見ている」。

米国では2001年9月11日の同時多発テロや1989年のサンフランシスコ地震などの異常事態の後に，広い範囲で夢の変化が起きたことが報告された。だがこれほど大規模なドリームサージは記録にない。今回のドリームサージは世界規模でかつSNS時代に起きたという点で前例がなく，これは夢の内容をすぐに研究できることを意味している。このパンデミックは，夢にかかわる出来事として未曾有の事態なのだ。

しかし，これは正確にはどういう現象なのだろうか。なぜ夢はそんなに急激に変化したのか。それを明らかにするため，*Dreaming*誌の編集長でハーバード大学の助教バレット（Deirdre Barrett）は2020年3月22日の週にCOVID-19の夢についてのオンライン調査を始めた。サンフランシスコのベイエリアに住むアーティストであるグレイブリー姉妹（Erin and Grace Gravley）はパンデミックの夢を記録してイラストで表現するサイトIDreamofCovid.comを開設した。COVID-19関連の夢に関するツイートを収集するボット@CovidDreamsの運用も始まった。宗教心理学者で，夢についての報告を集めたスリープ・アンド・ドリーム・データベースを運営しているバルクリー（Kelly Bulkeley）は，英国の調査会社YouGovを通じて米国の成人2477人の調査を実施した。また，かつて私の学生だったマギル大学ポスドク研究員のソロモノバ（Elizaveta Solomonova）は，カナダのオタワにある王立精神保健研究所のロビラード（Rebecca Robillard）らとともに調査を実施し，12 歳以上の 968 人（大半が北米在住）から回答を得た。これらの調査の結果はまだ論文になっていないが，オンラインでの予備的な報告には，夢の急激な増加や驚くほどの多様さ，心の健康への影響が示されている。

バルクリーの 3 日間の調査によって，3 月には 29%の米国人が普段より多くの夢を想起したことが明らかになった。ソロモノバとロビラードによれば，回答者の 37%がパンデミックの夢を見ており，その多くは何らかのタスクを完遂できない（例えば車がうまく運転できない），あるいは他人に脅かされたという内容だった。SNS の投稿も，こうした結果を裏づけている。ツイッターのアカウント @monicaluhar は「準備ができないまま，秋に補助教員として学校に戻る夢を見た。生徒はソーシャルディスタンシングをきちんと取れず，教員は授業を時差制にすることも個別に対面授業をすることもできなかった」と書きこんだ。またアカウント @therealbeecarey は「携帯電話がウイルスに感染し，保存していた写真がランダムにインスタグラムに大量投稿された。これまでで一番不安になった」とツイートした。

より最近の研究では，夢の中で経験する感情や健康への不安に質的な変化が起きていることが明らかになった。社会的隔離下にあるブラジルの成人が報告した夢の記述には，怒り，悲しみ，汚染，清潔さなどに関連する単語が高い割合で含まれていた。フィンランドの 810 人の夢に関する報告をテキストマイニングの手法で分析したところ，ほとんどの単語クラスターに不安を示す言葉が多数含まれていた。55%がソーシャルディスタンシングへの配慮のなさや高齢者の苦しみなどパンデミックに直接かかわるものであり，こうした感情は，日中強いストレスを感じている人により多く見られた。中国の武漢で COVID-19 患者のケアのために招集された看護師 100 人に対する調査では 45%が悪夢を経験していた。これは中国の精神科の外来患者が生涯に悪夢を経験する割合の 2 倍で，一般集団の悪夢障害（悪夢のために必要な睡眠がとれない状態）の有病率である 5% より何倍も高い。

こうした夢の急増には，明らかに何らかの基本的な生物学的・社会的な変化が関与していると思われる。ドリームサージの発生や持続をもたらしていると考えられる要因が少なくとも 3 つある。①通常の睡眠スケジュールが妨げられてレム睡眠が増え，そのため夢の量も増えたこと，②感染の恐怖やソーシャルディスタンシングによって夢の感情調節機能に負荷がかかっていること，③ソーシャルメディアとマスコミがドリームサージに対する市民の反応を増幅していることである。

レム睡眠が増え夢も増えた

ドリームサージが起きた理由の 1 つが，ロックダウンの実施によって睡眠パターンが突然変化したことにあるのは明白だ。初期の文献は中国人，なかでも最前線で働く人の間で不眠症が増えたことを示している。これとは対照的に，外出禁止のために長距離通勤がなくなり睡眠が改善された人も多かった。中国での調査によれば，ベッドにいる時間が平均 46 分増え，睡眠時間は全体で 34 分長くなった。フィンランドでは，約 54%の人々がロックダウンの開始後に

この記事の読み方

2020 年初めに始まった COVID-19 のパンデミックによって私たちの生活は一変した。感染の不安や恐怖はもとより，外出や社会的接触の制限，リモートワーク，マスクの着用とソーシャルディスタンシングの遵守などなど。本記事は，それらが私たちの睡眠や夢にどのような影響を与えつつあるかについての緊急リポートである。調査データがツイッターやインスタグラムなど SNS を通して収集されている点も特徴的。まさにその時にしかできない種類の調査研究だ。

調査からわかったのは，睡眠時間が大幅に増え，レム睡眠も，夢を見る頻度も大幅に増えた（著者はこれを dream surge と呼んでいる）こと。当然ながら，夢の内容もパンデミックに関係したものが多くなった。

掲載部分では，データの収集方法と分析手法，そして収集された夢の特徴的内容をかなり詳しく述べたあと，これらの夢や悪夢がどのような適応的機能を持ちうるのかを議論している。

睡眠時間が長くなったと答えた。2020 年 3 月 13 日から 27 日までの米国人の睡眠時間は全国で総じて約 20%増加し，特に通勤時間が長いメリーランド州やニュージャージー州で最大の増加となった。

睡眠時間が長いほど夢も増える。睡眠検査室で 9.5 時間以上眠った人は，一般的な 8 時間睡眠の場合より覚えている夢が多かった。長く眠ると，比例してレム睡眠（急速眼球運動睡眠）の時間も長くなる。人はレム睡眠の間に，最も鮮明で感情を伴う夢を見る。

スケジュールにゆとりがあると，通常より遅い朝の時間に夢を見る可能性が高くなる。朝はレム睡眠の時間が長く眼球運動も活発になるため，奇妙な夢が多くなる。夢に関するツイートにはこうした特徴がよく表れている。「私は新型コロナウイルスに感染した女の赤ちゃんの世話をしていた。とても鮮明でリアルな夢だった」などだ。朝の遅い時間のレム睡眠で夢が増えることには，複数のプロセスが関与している。睡眠は深い眠りと浅い眠りを 90 分ごとに繰り返すが，回復のための深い眠りが足りてくるにつれ，レム睡眠へと移行する圧力が増す。一方，24 時間周期の深部体温リズムと関連した概日リズムのため，睡眠の後半にはレム睡眠の傾向が急激に高まり，午前中はずっと高いままだ。

パンデミックが始まってから，多くの人がより長く，より遅くまで眠るようになった。中国では就寝時刻が 1 週間の平均で 26 分，起床時刻は 72 分遅くなった。この数字は，イタリアでは 41 分と 73 分，米国の大学生では 30 分と 42 分だ。また，通勤通学の必要がないのでベッドでぐずぐずしやすくなり，夢を思い返す人が多くなった。朝型から夜型に変わった人もいるが，夜型の人は一般にレム睡眠が多く，悪夢を見やすい。また，数日から数週間に及ぶ睡眠不足による睡眠負債が解消されて夜中に目を覚ましやすくなり，より多くの夢を思い出すようになった。

夢が正常に機能しない

COVID-19 に関する夢の多くは，感染への恐怖やソーシャルディスタンシングの困難を直接または間接に反映している。普段でも私たちは新しい経験についての夢を見ることが多い。例えばフランス語の速習プログラムを始めるとフランス語に関する夢を多く見る。研究者の多くは，断片的な経験の再生はレム睡眠および夢の機能的役割の１つだと考えている。夢のなかでの経験の再生が現実世界での問題解決に寄与しているのだ。ほかにも前日の出来事をより長期の記憶として定着させる，それらの出来事を日々の生活の文脈に則して位置づける，感情の調節を助けるといった機能がある。

夢が創造的な仕事の実現に役立った例については，大量の研究報告がある。レム睡眠は多岐にわたる記憶へのアクセスを必要とする問題の解決に有効であることが実証研究でも示されている。今回のドリームサージでCOVID-19に対処する創造的あるいはヘンテコな方法が登場する夢が非常に多いのは，これで説明がつくかもしれない。ある調査の回答者は「私はCOVID-19を予防または治療できるクリームを探していた。そして，その最後の１瓶を手に入れた」と答えた。

このほか研究者の多くが主張している夢の機能として，恐怖の記憶の消去と社会的状況のシミュレーションがある。これらは感情の制御と関連しており，今回急増した夢の中にパンデミックの恐怖とソーシャルディスタンシングの困難が頻繁に登場する理由を説明できそうだ。報道されている夢の多くに，感染や収入減，ソーシャルディスタンシングを恐れる反応が含まれている。「妊娠検査とコロナの検査で陽性になった。（中略）心配でたまらない」といったものだ。脅威は津波や宇宙人などの隠喩的なイメージの形を取ることもある。ゾンビもよく出てくるし，虫やクモなどの小さな生き物のイメージも広く見受けられる。「私の足はアリに覆われ，足の裏には５～６匹の毒グモが入り込んでいた」などだ。

直接的，あるいは隠喩的なイメージを理解する方法の１つは，夢はその人の最大の懸念を表しており，抱いた感情は似ているが主題としては別の出来事についての記憶を呼び出していると考えることだ。こうした文脈化は心的外傷後ストレス障害（PTSD）による悪夢では明確で，攻撃されたときの恐怖などのトラウマに対する反応が，津波などの自然災害に直面したときの恐怖として描かれたりする。夢と悪夢についてのパイオニアで，同時多発テロ後の夢について研究したボストンの精神分析医，故ハルトマン（Ernest Hartmann）は，こうした文脈化によって古い経験と新しい経験を 1 つに編みあげることが適応を助けるのだとした。統合がうまくいけば，将来のトラウマに対して高い回復力を持つ，より安定した記憶の体系が構築される。

Tore Nielsen
カナダのモントリオール大学の精神医学教授。夢と悪夢を専門とする研究室を主宰している。

Nap Like a Genius

天才のようにまどろめ
エジソンに学ぶ
半覚醒状態のひらめき

B.ステッカ（サイエンスライター）

眠りのきわから自分をたたき起こし，創造的アイデアを得たとされるエジソン
この方法は私たち凡人でも機能する可能性がある

KEY CONCEPTS

眠りと覚醒の境

■発明王エジソンは眠りに入ると手に持ったボールが床に落ちて目が覚めるようにして，浅い眠りの間に浮かんだアイデアを思い出していたとされる。

■実際，入眠時の半覚醒状態に創造性とひらめきが働く期間が存在することが近年の研究で示された。

■うつらうつらしているときに頭に浮かんだアイデアをうまく引き出せば，現実に役立つかもしれない。眠りと覚醒の境界域を探る研究が進んでいる。

日経サイエンス 2022年8月号，SCIENTIFIC AMERICAN April 2022

Thomas Edison was famously opposed to sleeping. In an 1889 interview published in Scientific American, the ever energetic inventor of the lightbulb claimed he never slept more than four hours a night. Sleep was, he thought, a waste of time.

Yet Edison may have relied on slumber to spur his creativity. The inventor is said to have napped while holding a ball in each hand, presuming that, as he fell asleep, the orbs would fall to the floor and wake him. This way he could remember the sorts of thoughts that come to us as we are nodding off, which we often do not recall.

Sleep researchers now suggest that Edison might have been on to something. A study published recently in Science Advances reports that we have a brief period of creativity and insight in the semilucid state that occurs just as we begin to drift into sleep, a sleep phase called N1, or non-rapid-eye-movement sleep stage 1. The findings imply that if we can harness that liminal haze between sleep and wakefulness—known as a hypnagogic state—we might recall our bright ideas more easily.

Inspired by Edison, Delphine Oudiette of the Paris Brain Institute and her colleagues presented 103 participants with mathematical problems that had a hidden rule that allowed them to be solved much faster. The 16 people who cracked the clue right away were then excluded from the study. The rest were given a 20-minute break period and asked to relax in a reclined position while holding a drinking glass in their right hand. If it fell, they were then asked to report what they had been thinking prior to letting go.

Throughout the break, subjects underwent polysomnography, a technology that monitors brain, eye and muscle activity to assess a person's state of wakefulness. This helped to determine which subjects were awake rather than in N1 or if they were in N2—the next, slightly deeper phase of our sleep.

Vocabulary

［タイトル］ **nap** うたた寝する

opposed to ～に反対である，～に否定的な

slumber うたた寝，まどろみ
spur 拍車をかける，刺激する
presume 推定する
orb 球
that way そのようにして
nod off うとうとする，うつらうつらする

on to something 何かに気づいている
brief 短時間の
insight 洞察，ひらめき
semilucid 半覚醒
drift into ～に陥る
non-rapid-eye-movement sleep ノンレム睡眠
imply 示唆する，意味する
harness 活用する
liminal 識閾の，境目の
wakefulness 覚醒
haze ぼんやりした状態
hypnagogic state ヒプナゴジア，半覚醒状態
▶この記事の読み方

present 提示する
participant 被験者，実験参加者
crack the clue 手がかりをつかむ
exclude 除外する
let go 手放す，取り落とす

polysomnography 睡眠ポリグラフ検査
subject 被験者

After the break, the study subjects were presented with the math problems again. Those who had dozed into N1 were nearly three times more likely to crack the hidden rule as others who had stayed awake throughout the experiment—and nearly six times more likely to do so as people who had slipped into N2. This "eureka moment," as the authors call it, did not occur immediately. Rather it happened after many subsequent attempts to solve the math problem, which is consistent with previous research on insight and sleep.

It's less clear that Edison's technique of dropping objects to ward off deeper sleep works. Of the 63 subjects who dropped the glass as they drowsed, 26 did so after they had already passed through N1 sleep. Still, the findings suggest that we do have a creative window just before falling asleep.

Oudiette says that, like Edison, her personal experience with sleep inspired the study. "I've always had a lot of hypnagogic experiences, dreamlike experiences that have fascinated me for a long time," she says. "I was quite surprised that almost no scientists have studied this period in the past two decades."

A study published in 2018 found that a brief period of "awake quiescence," or quiet resting, increased the odds of discovering the same mathematical rule used in Oudiette's experiment. And psychologist Penny Lewis of Cardiff University in Wales suggests that both rapid-eye-movement (REM) sleep—the phase in which our eyes dart back and forth and most dreams occur—and non-REM sleep work together to encourage problem-solving.

Yet for the most part, Oudiette is not aware of any other research specifically looking at the influence of sleep onset on creativity. She does, however, point to plenty of historical examples of this phenomenon.

Vocabulary

doze 居眠りする，うたた寝する
eureka moment エウレカモーメント
▶この記事の読み方
subsequent 以後の

ward off 防ぐ，避ける
drowse うとうとする
creative window 創造的活動の時間枠

awake quiescence 目覚めた安静状態
odds 見込み，公算
rapid-eye-movement (REM) sleep レム睡眠
dart back and forth きょろきょろと動く
encourage 促進する

for the most part 概して
onset 開始，始まり

"Alexander the Great and [Albert] Einstein potentially used Edison's technique, or so the legend goes," she says. "And some of the dreams that have inspired great discoveries could be hypnagogic experiences rather than night dreams. One famous example is the chemist August Kekulé finding the ring structure of benzene after seeing a snake biting its own tail in a 'half-sleep' period when he was up working late." Surrealist painter Salvador Dalí also used a variation of Edison's method: he held a key over a metal plate as he went to sleep, which clanged to wake him as he dropped it, supposedly inspiring his artistic imagery.

"This study gives us simultaneous insight into consciousness and creativity," says Adam Haar Horowitz of the M.I.T. Media Lab, who has devised technology to interact with hypnagogic states but did not collaborate with Oudiette's team. "Importantly," he adds, "it's the kind of study that you can go ahead and try at home yourself. Grab a metal object, lie down, focus hard on a creative problem, and see what sort of eureka moments you can encounter."

For University of California, Santa Barbara, psychologist Jonathan Schooler, who also was not involved with the project, the study does not necessarily prove that just anyone will be able to mine their creativity during this early phase of somnolence. As he points out, "residing in the 'sweet zone' might have also simply refreshed the study participants, making it easier for them to solve the problem later." But Schooler acknowledges there may be something very solid in the study's findings. "The new results suggest there is a creative sleep sweet spot during which individuals are asleep enough to access otherwise inaccessible elements but not so far gone the material is lost," he says.

Despite its reputation as the brain's period of "shutting off," sleep is, neurologically speaking, an incredibly active process. Brain cells fire by the billions, help to reactivate and store memories, and, it seems, allow us to conjure our

Vocabulary

so the legend goes 言い伝えによればそうである
ring structure 環状構造
clang ガチャンと音を立てる

simultaneous 同時の
consciousness 意識
devise 考案する
go ahead and try 進んで試す

involved with ～に関わる
mine 掘り出す, 引き出す
somnolence 眠気
reside in ～にある, ～にいる
acknowledge 認める
solid 確かな
otherwise それ以外では
inaccessible 手が届かない
far gone 深く寝入る
material 情報, 内容

shutting off 遮断, 休止
neurologically speaking 神経科学的に言えば
fire 発火する
by the billions 数十億個単位で
conjure 思いつく, 生み出す

mental creations.

Oudiette hopes not only to confirm her findings in future research but also to determine if focusing on our hypnagogic state might help solve real-world tasks and problems by harnessing the creative potential of that liminal period between sleep and wakefulness. Additionally, she and her group are considering the potential of brain-computer interfaces to precisely identify brain-wave patterns associated with the onset of sleep, allowing the precise identification of when people should be woken up during their moments of putative insight.

"We could even teach people how to reach this creative state at will," Oudiette envisions. "Imagine playing sounds when people are reaching the right state and other sounds when they are going too far into sleep. Such a method could teach them how to recognize the creative state and how to reach it."

Vocabulary

brain-computer interface ブレイン・マシン・インターフェース
putative 想定される, 推定上の

at will 意のままに
envision 思い描く

エジソン（Thomas Edison）が眠りを嫌ったことはよく知られている。電球の生みの親として万人に知られるこのエネルギッシュな発明家は，1889年の本誌 SCIENTIFIC AMERICAN に掲載されたインタビュー記事のなかで，一晩に4時間以上眠ったことはないと述べた。睡眠は時間の無駄だ――彼はそう考えていた。

だが一方で，彼はその創造性の発露をうたた寝に頼っていたようだ。昼寝をする際に両手に1個ずつボールを持ち，眠りに入るとボールが床に落ちて目が覚めるようにしたといわれている。そのようにして，うつらうつらしているときに頭に浮かんだ考えのたぐいを，つまりたいていはそれきりになってしまうアイデアを，思い出すことができたのだろう。

現代の睡眠研究に照らすと，エジソンはいいところに気づいていたといえそうだ。最近の *Science Advances* 誌に掲載された研究は，人が「ノンレム睡眠ステージ1（N1）」という浅い眠りに落ち始める段階では意識が半ば残っており，創造性とひらめきが働く短い期間が存在すると報告している。こうした発見は，うまくすれば睡眠と覚醒の境目をなすぼんやりした状態〔専門用語ではヒプナゴジア（入眠時における半覚醒状態）という〕から秀逸なアイデアをもっとうまく引き出せる可能性があることを意味している。

仏パリ脳研究所のウディエット（Delphine Oudiette）らはエジソンの逸話に触発され，ある実験をした。103人の被験者に数学の問題をいくつか提示する。これらの問題には共通の規則性が隠れていて，それに気づけばより早く解くことができる。そこにすぐに気づいて問題を解いた16人を実験から除外した後，残りの被験者に20分間の休憩を与えて，リクライニングチェアでくつろいでもらった。ただしガラスのコップを右手に持ちながら休んでもらう。うとうとしてコップを落とした場合，その被験者にコップを取り落とす前に何を考えていたかを尋ねた。

休憩の間，ポリソムノグラフィー（睡眠ポリグラフ）で被験者の脳と眼球，筋肉の活動をモニターし，覚醒の程度を評価した。これに基づいて，被験者が目覚めていたのか，あるいはN1やN2（N1よりも少し深い眠り）の状態にあったのかを判定した。

休憩の後，被験者は再び数学の問題に取り組んだ。N1 状態でまどろんでいた人はずっと目を覚ましていた人よりも，問題に隠された規則性に気づく率が 3 倍近く高く，N2 の眠りに落ちた人に比べると 6 倍に近かった。ただし，研究チームが「エウレカモーメント」と呼ぶこの瞬間はボーっとしているだけではやってこない。数学の問題に挑戦する試みを何度も繰り返した後に生じた。これは，ひらめきと睡眠に関する先行研究と整合している。

持っていた物体を落として熟睡に陥るのを避けるというエジソンの方法がうまくいくかどうかについては，やや不明瞭だ。休憩中にコップを取り落とした 63 人の被験者のうち 26 人は，その時点ですでに N1 の眠りにあった。それでもこの研究は，人が眠りに落ちる直前に創造的活動の時間枠を持っていること

この記事の読み方

記事の冒頭には，木陰の草むらに横たわって昼寝するエジソンの写真が見開き 2 ページにわたって掲載されている（151 ページ参照）。エジソンの隣では，ハーディング大統領が椅子に座って新聞を読んでいる。さらに，研究室で仮眠をとるエジソンの写真も掲載されている。エジソンは短眠者の代表のように言われるが，眠りたい時には場所を選ばず，断固眠っていたことがわかる。

タイトル「天才のようにまどろめ」とこれらの写真には，だれでも興味をそそられる。記事では，エジソンの例にならい，ひらめきを得るために入眠時のノンレム睡眠の第 1 段階，hypnagogic state（半覚醒の状態）をいかに利用するかが解説されている。

insight は問題解決の領域では「洞察」と訳されることが多いが，ここでは「ひらめき」という訳語のほうがぴったりくる。eureka moment は，ひらめきの瞬間のこと。“Eureka!” は「わかったぞ！」「そうか！」を意味するギリシャ語。アルキメデスが風呂に入っていてひらめきを得た時に発したことばとされる（後世の作話だろうが）。

なお，この記事は全文を掲載してある。

を示唆している。

ウディエットは彼女もエジソンと同様，眠りによって自身の研究にヒントを得た経験があるという。「夢に似た半覚醒のヒプナゴジック体験を何度もしたことがあり，これについてずっと興味を持っていた。私たちの研究以前の20年間にこの入眠時期について調べた科学者がほとんどいなかったのは非常な驚きだった」。

2018年に論文発表されたある研究は，短時間の「目覚めた安静状態」によって，ウディエットが実験で用いたのと同じ数学的規則性に被験者が気づきやすくなることを見いだした。また英カーディフ大学の心理学者ルイス（Penny Lewis）は，レム睡眠（眼球の急速な動きを伴う眠りで，夢を見ているのは大半がこの時期）とノンレム睡眠の両方が問題解決を促進しているのだと提唱している。

だがこれらを除くと，入眠が創造性に及ぼす影響に注目して調べた研究例は見当たらないとウディエットはいう。一方，この現象に関する歴史的な事例は数多いと指摘する。

「言い伝えによれば，アレキサンダー大王とアインシュタインがエジソンの方法を使っていた可能性がある。また，大発見のきっかけを与えた夢のいくつかは，夜中に見た夢ではなく，眠りに入る半覚醒状態での体験だったと考えられる。有名な例に，化学者のケクレ（August Kekulé）が夜遅くまで仕事をして“半ば眠った”状態になったときに，自分の尾を咬む蛇の姿が頭に浮かんで，ベンゼンの環状構造を思いついたという話がある」。シュルレアリスムの画家ダリ（Salvador Dalí）もエジソンの方法の変種を使っていた。眠る前に鍵を手に持ち，それが落ちると下の金属板に当たって目が覚めるようにした。芸術的イメージのヒントを得ようとしたのだろう。

入眠時半覚醒状態を探る技術を開発したマサチューセッツ工科大学メディアラボのホロウィッツ（Adam Haar Horowitz）はウディエットらの研究を「意識と創造性についての知見を与えてくれる」と評する。「重要なことに，この種の試みは一般人が自宅で行うこともできる。金属製の物を手にして横になり，創造力を要する問題に意識を集中して考え，どんなエウレカモーメントが訪れるかを見ればよい」。

カリフォルニア大学サンタバーバラ校の心理学者スクーラー（Jonathan Schooler）に言わせると，ウディエットらの研究は誰もがみなこの入眠の初期フェーズから創造性を引き出せると証明しているわけではない。彼が指摘するように，「被験者は“心地よい”休憩を取ってリフレッシュし，その後に問題を解くのが容易になっただけかもしれない」。だがスクーラーはこの研究が非常に確かな発見を含んでいると認める。「創造的な眠りの時期があり，当人は眠っているのだが，そこで頭に浮かんだすべてが失われるほど深い眠りではなく，それ以外では手が届かない要素を引き出せるスイートスポットが存在することを示唆している」という。

睡眠は一般に脳の“休止期間”であるととらえられているが，神経科学的には信じがたいほど活発なプロセスだ。数十億個単位の脳細胞が発火し，記憶を再生・固定しており，さらには知的創作物を生み出すことも可能にしているようだ。

ウディエットは今後の研究で今回の発見を確かめるだけでなく，半覚醒状態に注目して睡眠と覚醒の境をなす時期の創造力を活用することが実世界の課題や問題の解決に役立つかどうかを見極めたいと考えている。加えて，入眠に伴う脳波パターンを正確にとらえるブレイン・マシン・インターフェースの可能性を考えており，眠りかけた人をいつ起こせば半覚醒状態のひらめきを手に入れられるかを正しく特定したいという。

「この創造的状態に自由にアクセスする方法を考案できるかもしれない」とウディエットは夢見ている。「眠りが適切な状態に達したらある音を鳴らし，眠りが深くなりすぎたら別の音を鳴らすというのはどうだろう。そうすれば，本人が創造的な半覚醒状態を認識して，そこに達する方法を体得できるだろう」。

Bret Stetka
米ニューヨークを拠点に活動するサイエンスライターで，メッドスケープニューロロジー（WebMDの一部門）の編集担当役員を務めている。*Wired* 誌，*Atlantic* 誌，ナショナル・パブリック・ラジオなどに寄稿・出演。2005年バージニア大学医学部卒業。

The Science of Genius

創造性の起源

D. K. シモントン
(米カリフォルニア大学デービス校)

あらゆる分野での卓越した創造性は
共通の形質と発見プロセスに由来しているようだ

KEY CONCEPTS

遺伝と経験と試行錯誤

■天才は2通りの方法でとらえられてきた。1つは卓越した業績への評価，もう1つは並外れた知能だ。後者よりは前者の基準の方が，より有用な定義をもたらす。

■天才を生み出す要因には遺伝と経験がある。創造的な業績は，特定分野での知識習得なしには達成できないが，限られた専門知識で短期間に多くの業績を上げるには遺伝的要因が助けになる。

■天才は，潜在的にはネガティブな特性を精神病患者と共有しているが，こうした特性が特定のポジティブな特性と組み合わさる結果，精神病ではなく創造性が生み出される。

■科学界の天才は芸術界の天才とは異なる専門知識を持っているが，すべての創造的天才は，ある共通のプロセスをたどっている可能性がある。持続的なある種の試行錯誤だ。

日経サイエンス 2013 年 6 月号，SCIENTIFIC AMERICAN MIND November/December 2012

Identifying genius is a dicey venture. Consider, for example, this ranking of "The Top 10 Geniuses" I recently stumbled across on Listverse.com. From first to last place, here are the honorees: Johann Wolfgang von Goethe, Leonardo da Vinci, Emanuel Swedenborg, Gottfried Wilhelm von Leibniz, John Stuart Mill, Blaise Pascal, Ludwig Wittgenstein, Bobby Fischer, Galileo Galilei and Madame De Staël.

What about Albert Einstein instead of Swedenborg? Some of the living might also deserve this appellation— Stephen Hawking comes to mind. A female genius or two might make the cut, perhaps Marie Curie or Toni Morrison. And if a chess champion, Fischer, is deemed worthy, other geniuses outside the arts and sciences ought to deserve consideration—Napoleon Bonaparte as a military genius, Nelson Mandela as a political genius or Bill Gates as an entrepreneurial genius, to name a few candidates.

All these questions and their potential answers can make for some lively cocktail party conversations. What they reveal is how little we understand about the origins of intellectual and creative eminence. Explorations of this age-old debate have long sought to tease out the common features of geniuses working in disparate domains. The existence of unifying threads— including genetic factors, unusually broad interests and a link with psychopathy—suggests that the mind of a genius has a discernible shape and disposition.

Ultimately the goal is to explain how an eminent thinker arrives at his or her world-changing moment, or moments, of insight. Although such breakthroughs often seem to appear in a flash, the underlying mechanisms are likely to be much more orderly. According to one theory I helped to develop, a genius hunts widely—almost blindly—for a solution to a problem, exploring

Vocabulary

［タイトル］**genius** 天才

dicey あやふやな
venture 企て
stumble across 偶然見つける

the living 生きている人々
appellation 呼称，称号
make the cut 要件を満たす
arts and sciences 学芸分野
entrepreneurial 起業家の

make for ～を生み出す，～に役立つ
eminence 卓越性
exploration 探求
age-old 長年の，昔からの
tease out 引き出す
disparate さまざまな
unifying thread 共通する要素
psychopathy 精神病質
discernible 識別できる
disposition 傾向

insight 洞察，アイデア
in a flash ひらめきによって
orderly 秩序だった

dead ends and backtracking repeatedly before arriving at the ideal answer. If this line of research bears out, we can start to investigate whether genius can be cultivated, unleashing a wealth of new ideas for the benefit of all.

Vocabulary

dead end 袋小路
backtrack 後戻りする
bear out 正しいことがわかる
cultivate 育てる

The Meaning of Genius

The first hurdle in the study of genius is to settle on a working definition. The word itself harks back to ancient Roman mythology, according to which every male was born with a unique genius that served as a kind of guardian angel, and every female had a juno. Much later, after the Renaissance, the word became more exclusive in its application, with only a few people showing genius. Philosopher Immanuel Kant believed, for example, that a genius was someone who produced works that were both original and exemplary. The term did not acquire scientific meaning until the late 19th century, when psychologists came to define genius in two distinct ways.

settle on 決める
working 暫定的な
hark back to ～を思い出させる
genius ゲニウス
guardian angel 守護天使，守護霊
juno ユーノー
exclusive 限定的な
application 適用，使い方
exemplary 模範となる
distinct 異なる

The first approach was to identify genius with exceptional achievement, as Kant did. These accomplishments elicit admiration and emulation from other experts in that field and often the world at large. Unquestioned examples of such works include Newton's Principia, Shakespeare's Hamlet, Tolstoy's War and Peace, Michelangelo's Sistine Chapel frescoes and Beethoven's Fifth Symphony. Even though this definition can be extended to encompass extraordinary leadership, such as military brilliance, and prodigious performance, including some chess grandmasters, most scientific research concentrates on outstanding creativity within the sciences or the arts, which will also be the focus here.

exceptional 並外れた
achievement 業績
accomplishment 偉業
elicit 引き出す，引き起こす
admiration 称賛
emulation 競争，対抗心
encompass 包含する
extraordinary 類まれな
brilliance 技量
prodigious 驚異的な

The second definition of genius coincided with the emergence of intelligence tests in the first half of the 20th century. A genius was someone who scored sufficiently high on a standard IQ test—usually landing in the top 1 percent, with a score above 140, as proposed by psychol-

coincide with ～と同時期に生まれる
emergence 出現
intelligence test 知能テスト

ogist Lewis Terman, the formulator of one of the original intelligence tests. These two definitions have little in common. Many persons with superlative IQs do not produce original and exemplary accomplishments. One example is Marilyn vos Savant, who was once certified by the Guinness Book of World Records as having the highest recorded IQ of any living person. Her weekly "Ask Marilyn" column for a Sunday newspaper supplement did not inspire a new genre of science, art or even journalism. And many exceptional achievers do not attain genius-level IQs. William Shockley, for example, received a Nobel Prize in Physics for coinventing the transistor yet had an IQ score well below 140. Exceptional achievement, then, seems the more useful measure.

Vocabulary

formulator 考案者
superlative 最高の
certify 認定する
Sunday newspaper supplement 新聞の日曜版
measure 尺度

Too often in popular writing, genius is conceived as a discrete category—this person is a genius, but that person is not. Yet just as people can vary in IQ, they can also differ in the magnitude of their creative achievements, with either a single notable contribution or a lifetime of prolific work. One such "one-hit wonder" is Gregor Mendel, who attained lasting fame for a single paper that reported his classic experiments in genetics. Had Mendel never taken an interest in breeding peas, his name would be unknown today. Charles Darwin's fame, in contrast, rests on far more than On the Origin of Species. Nobel laureate Max Born once said that Einstein "would be one of the greatest theoretical physicists of all time even if he had not written a single line on relativity." Hence, Darwin and Einstein exhibited greater genius than did Mendel. Accordingly, much research is devoted to assessing relative degrees of genius—most often gauged by creative productivity.

discrete 別個の
notable 際立った
prolific 多作の
one-hit wonder 一発屋
▶この記事の読み方
fame 名声
genetics 遺伝学
pea エンドウマメ
relativity 相対性
creative productivity 創造的生産性

Origins of Genius

Finding the sources of consummate creativity has occupied the minds of philosophers and scientists for centuries. In 1693 English poet John Dryden wrote, "Genius must be born, and never can be taught." Two and a half

consummate 途方もない，並外れた

centuries later French author Simone de Beauvoir countered, "One is not born a genius, one becomes a genius." The first scientific investigation devoted exclusively to genius concerned this precise issue. In 1869 Francis Galton published Hereditary Genius, in which he argued that genius is innate, based on his observations that geniuses tend to emerge from lineages that included other brilliant individuals. In response to criticisms, Galton later introduced the well-known nature-nurture issue. He conducted a survey of famous English scientists to discover some of the environmental variables involved in nurturing brilliance, and he examined factors such as birth order and education.

By the second half of the 20th century psychologists had moved to an extreme nurture position, in which creative genius rested solely on the acquisition of domain expertise. This idea was frequently expressed as the "10-year rule." Nobody can expect to reach the heights of creativity without mastering the necessary knowledge and skill because only experts can create—or so the thinking went. Indeed, Einstein learned lots of physics before he commenced his creative career.

This explanation cannot account for all the details, however. First, geniuses often spend less time acquiring domain expertise than their less creative colleagues. Studies have linked accelerated acquisition with long, prolific and high-impact careers. The 10-year rule is an average with tremendous variation around the mean. Further, major breakthroughs often occur in areas where the genius must create the necessary expertise from scratch. Telescopic astronomy did not exist until Galileo pointed his new instrument toward the night sky to discover what had never been seen before nor even expected. The moon had mountains, Jupiter had moons and the sun had spots!

Vocabulary

counter 反論する
Hereditary Genius 「遺伝的天才」
innate 生得的, 生来の
lineage 家系
nature-nurture issue 生まれか育ちか論争
▶この記事の読み方
environmental variable 環境要因

nurture 育ち, 環境要因
domain expertise 分野の専門知識
10-year rule 10年ルール
commence 開始する

account for 説明する
acquisition 習得
mean 平均
from scratch 一から
telescopic astronomy 望遠鏡天文学
spot 黒点

Second, geniuses are more likely to exhibit unusually wide interests and hobbies and to display exceptional versatility, often contributing to more than one domain of expertise. This tendency was true not only in the era of Renaissance men but is also evident today. According to a 2008 study, Nobel laureates in science are more involved in the arts than less eminent scientists. Given that geniuses likely do not sleep any less than the rest of us, these extraneous activities would seem to distract from a dogged focus on a narrow field of interest. Einstein slept even more hours than the norm, but he still took time off to play Bach, Mozart and Schubert on his violin. At times these avocational activities inspire major insights. Galileo was probably able to identify the lunar mountains because of his training in the visual arts, particularly in the use of chiaroscuro to depict light and shadow.

Vocabulary

versatility 多才
laureate 受賞者
given that ～ということを考慮すると
extraneous 無関係な
distract 気を散らす
dogged 粘り強い
norm 標準
avocational 余技の，本業以外の
chiaroscuro 明暗法

ある人物を天才であると特定することには，あやふやさが付きまとう。私が最近，Listverse.com で見つけた次のような「天才トップ 10」のランキングを例にとってみよう。10 位までにランクインした面々は以下の通り。ゲーテ，ダ・ヴィンチ，スウェーデンボルグ，ライプニッツ，ミル，パスカル，ヴィトゲンシュタイン，ボビー・フィッシャー（米国のチェスプレーヤー），ガリレオ，スタール夫人（フランスの作家）。

スウェーデンボルグの代わりにアインシュタインではどうだろう？　現役の何人かも天才の称号に値するだろう。例えばスティーブン・ホーキングが思い浮かぶ。女性の天才もあと 1 人か 2 人, 入れてもいいだろう。たぶんキュリー夫人かトニ・モリスン（米国のノーベル賞作家）。チェス・チャンピオンのフィッシャーがランクインするなら，学芸分野以外の天才も考慮に値するはずだ。候補を少し挙げると，軍事の天才ナポレオン，政治の天才ネルソン・マンデラ，起業の天才ビル・ゲイツといった具合だ。

このような設問や答えは，カクテルパーティーの会話を弾ませるのには役立つが，同時に，知的・創造的な卓越性に関する私たちの理解がいかに乏しいかも示している。さまざまな分野で活躍する天才たちに共通する特徴を見いだそうと，古くから探求が進められてきた。遺伝的要因，異様なまでの関心分野の広さ，精神病質との関連――。このような天才に共通する要素が存在することは，彼らの精神が識別可能な 1 つのパターンを持つことを示唆している。

こうした探求の最終的な目標は，卓越した思索者が一体どのようにして，世界を一変させるようなアイデアに到達するのかを説明することだ。そうした大発見は一瞬のひらめきでなされると思われがちだが，その根底にあるメカニズムは，ずっと秩序だったものである可能性が高い。私もその構築に関与した 1 つの理論によると，天才はある問題の解決法を広範囲に（ほとんど盲目的に）探し回り，袋小路を探り尽くし，繰り返し後戻りをした末に，ようやく理想的な答えにたどり着く。もしこの理論が正しければ，天才を育成し，万人のために新しいアイデアを生み出してもらうといったことも可能になるだろう。

天才の意味

天才を研究する上での最初のハードルとなるのは，その定義を決めることだ。天才（genius）という言葉は古代ローマの神話に由来する。それによると，あらゆる男性には生まれつき，守護霊のような役割を果たすゲニウス（Genius）がおり，あらゆる女性には守護神ユーノー（Juno）がいた。ずっと後のルネサンス期以降には，この言葉は限定的に使われるようになり，天才は一部の人のみが持つものとなった。例えば哲学者のカント（Immanuel Kant）は，天才とは創造的かつ賞賛すべき成果を生み出す人間であると位置づけた。天才という言葉が科学的な意味を持つようになったのは 19 世紀末になってからで，心理学者は天才を 2 通りの異なる方法で定義するようになった。

カントによるのと同様，天才を並外れたことを達成する者であるとするのが第一の定義だ。そうした偉業は斯界の他の人間，また往々にして世間全体に称賛と対抗心を巻き起こす。そうした偉業の紛れもない例としては，ニュート

この記事の読み方

原題は “The Science of Genius”（天才の科学）。邦題はリード文の説明のほうを採用して，「創造性の起源」にしてある。天才の創造性についてのベーシックな解説記事である。

記事では，天才を定義することの難しさを述べたあと，「生まれか育ちか論争」に言及している。この韻を踏んだ名文句，nature-nurture issue は 19 世紀後半にゴルトンが言い出したもの。遺伝 vs. 環境，先天性 vs. 後天性，あるいは生得性 vs. 獲得性の二分法をよく表現している。現在は，遺伝的な形質の発現には環境が大きく影響することがわかっているので，このような極端な二分法をとることは少ない。なお，掲載文以降では，天才特有の性格特性や思考スタイルが論じられている。

文中では，one-hit wonder（一発屋）の例としてメンデルが挙げられているが，誤解があるといけないので，ひと言補足。メンデルは自分の発見を 1 編の論文として発表はしたが，それが正当に評価されるようになるのは彼の死後，論文発表から 35 年経ってのことである。

ンの『プリンキピア』, シェイクスピアの『ハムレット』, トルストイの『戦争と平和』, ミケランジェロが描いたシスティーナ礼拝堂のフレスコ画，ベートーベンの交響曲第 5 番などがある。この定義は, 軍事面の技量に見られる類まれな指導力や, チェスのグランドマスターが持つ驚異的な戦績にも適用できるものの，天才についてのほとんどの研究は，学芸分野に対象を絞っている。本稿でもこれに的を絞ることにする。

天才の 2 つ目の定義は，20 世紀前半に知能テストとともに生まれた。初期の知能テストの 1 つを考案した心理学者ターマン（Lewis Terman）は，天才とは標準的な IQ テストで 140 以上の高スコアを記録する者であるとした。これら 2 つの定義には共通項がほとんどない。最高の IQ を持つ人の多くは，創造的で賞賛すべき偉業を達成しない。一例は，かつてギネスブックが，存命者の中で最高の IQ を持つと認定したヴォス・サヴァント（Marilyn vos Savant）だ。新聞の日曜版に彼女が毎週掲載したコラム「マリリンに聞け」は，学芸の新ジャンルはもとより，ジャーナリズムの新ジャンルさえ切り開かなかった。また，多くの並外れた業績の達成者は，天才レベルの IQ には届かない。トランジスタの共同発明者であるショックレー（William Shockley）はノーベル物理学賞を受賞したが，IQ は 140 を大きく下回っていた。こうしてみると，並外れた業績を上げた人を天才とするのが，定義としてより有用であると思われる。

学術論文ではない一般向けの文章では得てして，天才を離散的な存在，つまり人は天才であるかないかのどちらか一方であるとする。しかし実際には, IQ が人によって異なるように，創造的な業績のスケールも人によって異なり，単一の卓越した業績もあれば, 生涯にわたって築かれた膨大な業績もある。“一発屋”の例はメンデル（Gregor Mendel）だ。メンデルは古典的な遺伝学実験を報告した 1 本の論文で不滅の名声を勝ち得た。メンデルがエンドウマメの交配に興味を持たなかったなら, 彼は無名のまま終わっただろう。対照的にダーウィン（Charles Darwin）の名声は『種の起源』だけにとどまるものではない。ノーベル賞受賞者のボルン（Max Born）はかつてアインシュタイン（Albert Einstein）について,「相対性理論についてたとえ一行も書かなかったとしても，史上最大の理論物理学者の 1 人だろう」と述べた。ダーウィンやアインシュタインはメンデルよりも大きな天才を示したわけだ。このようなわけで, 多くの研究は創造の「生産性」によって，天才を比較・評価している。

天才の起源

哲学者や科学者は，何世紀もの間，並外れた創造性の源はどこに求められるのかを考えてきた。1693年, 英国の詩人ドライデン（John Dryden）は,「天才は生まれつきであり，天才を育てることは決してできない」と記した。その2世紀半後，フランスの作家ボーヴォワール（Simone de Beauvoir）は,「人は天才に生まれるのではなく，天才になるのだ」と反論した。天才をテーマとした最初の科学的研究は，まさにこの問題に関するものだった。1869年，英国の遺伝学者ゴルトン（Francis Galton）は『遺伝的天才』を著し，その中で，天才は他にも複数の優秀な個人を生んだ家系から出る傾向があるという所見に基づいて，天才は生来のものであると主張した。ゴルトンは後に批判に応えて，有名な「生まれか育ちか論争」の口火を切っている。彼は英国の有名な科学者たちを調べ，いくつかの環境要因が優秀さの養成に関係していることを発見し，出生の順番や教育といった要因を考察した。

20世紀後半，心理学者たちは，創造的な天才は，専門的な知識を身に付けることによってのみ生まれるとする，極端な後天性の立場に移っていた。この考え方はしばしば「10年ルール」と表現される。創造的な仕事は，専門家にしかできず，一般に優れた知識とスキルを獲得するには約10年かかると考えるのだ。現にアインシュタインは，創造的な業績を上げる前に，大量の物理学的知識を習得していた。

しかし，こうした見方ですべてを説明することはできない。第一に，天才はしばしば，他の専門家と比べて短時間で知識を習得する。複数の研究によれば，こうした加速的な習得が，長期にわたる膨大で影響力の大きい実績につながることが多い。10年ルールは平均の話であって，天才は10年もかからない。さらに，大発見はしばしば，天才が一から知識を生み出すことによってなされる。望遠鏡天文学は，ガリレオが自作の新しい道具を夜空に向けて，それまで見られもせず, 予想もされなかったものを発見するまで存在しなかった。彼の観察によって，月には山々があり，木星には複数の月があり，太陽に黒点があるとわかったのだ。

第二に，天才は，非常に幅広い関心や趣味を持っていたり，桁外れに多面的な才能を発揮したりして，しばしば複数の専門領域に貢献する。この傾向は，ルネサンス的教養人の時代だけでなく，現代にも当てはまる。2008 年のある研究によると，科学分野のノーベル賞受賞者は，通常の科学者よりも芸術に深く関わっている。天才の睡眠時間が凡人と変わらないとすると，こうした無関係な活動は専門分野への集中の妨げになるように思えるが，そうではない。アインシュタインの睡眠時間は平均より何時間も多かっただけでなく，さらにバイオリンでバッハやモーツァルトやシューベルトを演奏することにも時間を割いていた。こうした本業以外の活動から重要なアイデアがひらめくこともある。ガリレオが月の山々を確認できたのは，おそらく，視覚芸術，とりわけ光と影を描くための明暗法使用についての素養があったためだろう。

Dean Keith Simonton
米カリフォルニア大学デービス校の特別教授（心理学）。400 を超える論文や担当章の執筆に加え，“Great Flicks”（Oxford University Press，2011）をはじめ 10 数冊の著書がある。

心と社会

5

The “It” Factor

生まれながらの協力上手

G. スティックス
（SCIENTIFIC AMERICAN 編集部）

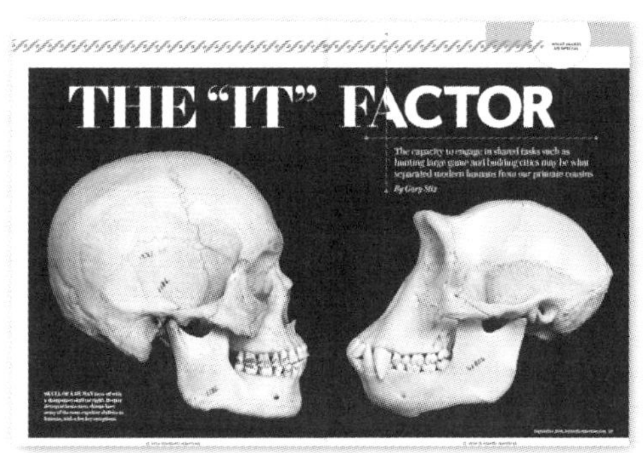

ともに獲物を狩ったり都市を築いたりといった共同作業を遂行できる能力が
ヒトと他の霊長類との違いなのかもしれない

KEY CONCEPTS

直観的な推察能力

■かつて，人間と他の動物との違いは道具を作ることと，様々な認知能力が総じて優れていることだと考えられていた。だがチンパンジーなどの類人猿の行動を詳しく観察した結果，この考え方は誤りであると判明した。

■チンパンジーは一般的な推論能力のテストで幼い子どもと同様の高得点を上げる。ただし，人間に生来備わっている社会的スキルの多くを欠いており，ヒトとは違って，複雑な社会を築くのに必要な大集団での協力をしない。

■ヒトとチンパンジーの認知能力を比較する研究によれば，人間を類人猿と異なるものにしている重要な違いは，他者が考えていることを直観的に理解する能力を進化させたことらしい。それによって，共通の目的に向かって力を合わせられるようになった。

日経サイエンス 2014 年 12 月号，SCIENTIFIC AMERICAN Septemter 2014

At a psychology laboratory in leipzig, germany, two toddlers eye gummy bears that lie on a board beyond their reach. To get the treats, both tots must pull in tandem on either end of a rope. If only one child pulls, the rope detaches, and they wind up with nothing.

A few miles away, in a plexiglass enclosure at Pongoland, the ape facility at the Leipzig Zoo, researchers repeat the identical experiment, but this time with two chimpanzees. If the primates pass the rope-and-board test, each one gets a fruit treat.

By testing children and chimps in this way, investigators hope to solve a vexing puzzle: Why are humans so successful as a species? *Homo sapiens* and *Pan troglodytes* share almost 99 percent of their genetic material. Why, then, did humans come to populate virtually every corner of the planet—building the Eiffel Tower, Boeing 747s and H-bombs along the way? And why are chimps still foraging for their supper in the dense forests of equatorial Africa, just as their ancestors did seven or so million years ago, when archaic humans and the great apes separated into different species?

As with any event that occurred on the time scale of evolution—hundreds of thousands or millions of years in the making—scientists may never reach a consensus on what really happened. For years the prevailing view was that only humans make and use tools and are capable of reasoning using numbers and other symbols. But that idea fell by the wayside as we learned more about what other primates are capable of A chimp, with the right coach, can add numbers, operate a computer and light up a cigarette.

At present, the question of why human behavior differs from that of the great apes, and how much, is still a matter of debate. Yet experiments such as the one in

Vocabulary

toddler よちよち歩きの幼児
eye 見つめる
gummy bears グミベア(クマの形をしたグミ)
treat おやつ, お菓子
tot 小さい子ども
in tandem 協力して
detach はずれる
wind up with nothing 何も得られずに終わる

plexiglass アクリル樹脂
enclosure 囲い
ape 類人猿
identical 同じ, 同一の
primate 霊長類

vexing 厄介な
species 生物種
Pan troglodytes チンパンジーの学名
genetic material 遺伝物質, ゲノム
populate 居住する
H-bomb 水爆
along the way これまでに
forage あさる, 探し回る
equatorial 赤道(付近)の, 熱帯の
archaic 原始の
great ape 大型類人猿

as with ～の場合と同様
evolution 進化
in the making 進行中の, 進化途上の
for years 長年
prevailing 支配的な, 一般的な
reasoning 推論
fall by the wayside 落伍する

Leipzig, under the auspices of the Max Planck Institute for Evolutionary Anthropology, have revealed a compelling possibility, identifying what may be a unique, but easy to overlook, facet of the human cognitive apparatus. From before their first birthday—a milestone some psychologists term "the nine-month revolution"—children begin to show an acute awareness of what goes on inside their mother's and father's heads. They evince this new ability by following their parents' gaze or looking where they point. Chimps can also figure out what is going on in a companion's mind to some degree, but humans take it one step further: infant and elder also have the ability to put their heads together to focus on what must be done to carry out a shared task. The simple act of adult and infant rolling a ball back and forth is enabled by this subtle cognitive advantage.

Some psychologists and anthropologists think that this melding of minds may have been a pivotal event that occurred hundreds of thousands of years ago and that shaped later human evolution. The ability of small bands of hunter-gatherers to work together in harmony ultimately set off a cascade of cognitive changes that led to the development of language and the spread of diverse human cultures across the globe.

This account of human psychological evolution, synthesized from bits and pieces of research on children and chimps, is speculative, and it has its doubters. But it provides perhaps the most impressively broad-ranging picture of the origins of cognitive abilities that make humans special.

The Ratchet Effect

The Max Planck Institute maintains the world's largest research facility devoted to examining the differences in behavior between humans and the great apes. Dozens of studies may be running at any one time. Researchers can draw subjects from a database of more than 20,000 children

Vocabulary

under the auspices of ～の後援(支援)のもと
compelling 実に興味深い
overlook 見逃す
facet 側面
cognitive apparatus 認知機構
milestone 節目, 転換点
"the nine-month revolution" 「９カ月革命」
acute 明敏な
evince 表す
gaze 視線
figure out 理解する
infant 幼児
elder 大人
shared 共通の
subtle わずかな
cognitive advantage 認知的利点

anthropologist 人類学者
meld 融合する
pivotal 極めて重要な
hunter-gatherer 狩猟採集民
set off 引き起こす
a cascade of 一連の
diverse 多様な

account 説明
bits and pieces of こまごまとした
speculative 推測の, 推論の

ratchet effect ラチェット効果
▶この記事の読み方
devoted to ～に特化した, ～に専門的に取り組む

and recruit chimpanzees or members of any of the other great ape species—orangutans, bonobos and gorillas—from the Wolfgang Köhler Primate Research Center at the Leipzig Zoo a few miles away.

The institute began 17 years ago, seven years after the reunification of Germany. Founding the institute required coming to grips with the tarnished legacy of German anthropology—and its association with Nazi racial theories and, in particular, the grisly human experiments performed in Auschwitz by Josef Mengele, who was a physician with a doctorate in anthropology. The institute's organizers went out of their way to recruit group leaders for genetics, primatology, linguistics and other disciplines who were not native Germans.

One of them was Michael Tomasello, a tall, bearded psychologist and primatologist. Now 64, he grew up in a small citrus-growing city at the epicenter of the Florida peninsula. He began his academic career at the University of Georgia with a dissertation on the way toddlers acquire language. While he was doing his doctorate in the 1970s, linguists and psychologists often cited language as exhibit number one for human exceptionalism in the animal world.

Tomasello's doctoral thesis chronicled how his almost two-year-old daughter learned her first verbs. The emergence of proto words—"play play" or "ni ni"—revealed a natural inclination of the young child to engage in trial-and-error testing of language elements, an exercise that gradually took on the more conventional structuring of grammar and syntax. This learning process stood in contrast to the ideas of Noam Chomsky and other linguists who contended that grammar is somehow genetically hardwired in our brains—an explanation that struck Tomasello as reductionist. "Language is such a complicated thing that it couldn't have evolved like the opposable thumb," he says.

Vocabulary

reunification 再統一
found 設立する
come to grips with ～と向き合う，～に真剣に取り組む
tarnished 汚された
association つながり，関連
Nazi racial theories ナチスの人種差別的イデオロギー
grisly おぞましい，身の毛のよだつ
physician 医師
doctorate 博士号
go out of one's way 特別の努力を払う，わざわざ～する
genetics 遺伝学
primatology 霊長類学
linguistics 言語学
discipline 学問分野

bearded あごひげを生やした
citrus-growing 柑橘類を栽培する
epicenter 中心
dissertation 学位論文
exhibit number one 証拠第1号
human exceptionalism 人間例外主義

doctoral thesis 博士論文
chronicle (時間を追って)記録する
verb 動詞
emergence 出現
proto word 前言語
engage in ～を行う，～に取り組む
take on 帯びる，獲得する
grammar 文法
syntax 構文
stand in contrast to ～と対照的である
contend 強く主張する
hardwired 生まれつき備わっている
strike someone as ～という印象を(人に)与える
reductionist 還元主義的な
opposable thumb 母指対向性

His work on language broadened his thinking about the relation between culture and human evolution. Tomasello realized that selective forces alone, acting on physical traits, could not explain the emergence of complex tools, language, mathematics and elaborate social institutions in the comparatively brief interval on the evolutionary time line since humans and chimps parted ways. Some innate mental capacity displayed by hominins (modern humans and our extinct relatives) but absent in nonhuman primates must have enabled our forebears to behave in ways that vastly hastened the ability to feed and clothe themselves and to flourish in any environment, no matter how forbidding.

Vocabulary

selective force 選択圧
physical trait 身体的形質，身体特性
elaborate 複雑な，精緻な
social institution 社会制度
part ways 分かれる
innate 生得的な，生来の
hominin ホミニン（ヒト族）
extinct 絶滅した
forebear 祖先
hasten 加速する，促進する
flourish 繁栄する
forbidding 過酷な

When Tomasello moved to a professorship at Emory University during the 1980s, he availed himself of the university's Yerkes primate research center to look for clues to this capacity in studies comparing the behaviors of children with those of chimps. The move set in motion a multidecade quest that he has continued at Max Planck since 1998.

avail oneself of ～を利用する
clue 手がかり
move 手だて，戦略
set in motion ～の口火を切る，～のきっかけとなる

In his studies of chimp learning, Tomasello noticed that apes do not ape each other the way humans imitate one another. One chimp might emulate another chimp using a stick to fetch ants out of a nest. Then others in the group might do the same. As Tomasello looked more closely, he surmised that chimps were able to understand that a stick could be used for "ant dipping," but they were unconcerned with mimicking one technique or another that might be used in hunting for the insects. More important, there was no attempt to go beyond the basics and then do some tinkering to make a new and improved ant catcher.

ape 猿真似する
emulate 真似る
fetch 取り出す，引き出す
surmise 推測する
"ant dipping"「アリ釣り」
mimick 真似る
tinkering 手直し

In human societies, in contrast, this type of innovation is a distinguishing characteristic that Tomasello calls a "ratchet effect." Humans modify their tools to make them better and then pass this knowledge along to their descen-

distinguishing 際立った，顕著な
modify 改良する
descendant 子孫
tweak 微調整

dants, who make their own tweaks—and the improvements ratchet up. What starts as a lobbed stone projectile invented to kill a mammoth evolves over the millennia into a slingshot and then a catapult, a bullet, and finally an intercontinental ballistic missile.

This cultural ratchet provides a rough explanation for humans' success as a species but leads to another question: What specific mental processes were involved in transmitting such knowledge to others? The answer has to begin with speculations about changes in hominin physiology and behavior that may have taken place hundreds of thousands of years ago. One idea—the social brain hypothesis, put forward by anthropologist Robin Dunbar of the University of Oxford—holds that group size, and hence cultural complexity, scales up as brains get bigger. And scientists know that by 400,000 years ago, *Homo heidelbergensis*, probably our direct ancestor, had a brain almost as large as ours.

Tomasello postulates that, equipped with a bigger brain and confronted with the need to feed a growing population, early hominins began careful strategizing to track and outwit game. The circumstances exerted strong selection pressures for cooperation: any member of a hunting party who was not a team player—taking on a carefully defined role when tracking and cornering an animal—would have been excluded from future outings and so might face an unremittingly bleak future. If one hunter was a bad partner, Tomasello notes, the rest of the group would then decide: "We won't do this again." In his view, what separated modern humans from the hominin pack was an evolutionary adaptation for hypersociality.

Vocabulary

ratchet up 徐々に増える
lobbed stone projectile 石投げ装置
slingshot ぱちんこ
intercontinental ballistic missile 大陸間弾道ミサイル

rough 大まかな
specific 具体的な, 特定の
speculation 推測
physiology 生理学, 生理機能
social brain hypothesis 社会脳仮説
▶この記事の読み方
put forward 提唱する
hold ～と考える
Homo heidelbergensis ホモ・ハイデルベルゲンシス

postulate 仮定する
confronted with ～に直面して
strategize 戦略を練る
outwit 出し抜く, 裏をかく
game 獲物
exert (圧力を)かける, 働かせる
selection pressure 選択圧
take on 引き受ける
corner 追い詰める
exclude 排除する
outing (狩りに)出かけること
unremittingly bleak お先真っ暗な, 暗澹たる
pack 集団, 群れ
adaptation 適応
hypersociality 優れて社会的な生活

ドイツのライプチヒにある心理学研究施設で，2 人の幼児が手の届かないところにある板に載せられたお菓子のグミベアを見つめている。このお菓子を手に入れるには，2 人がそれぞれロープの端をつかんで引っ張り，板を引き寄せねばならない。1 人だけで引っ張るとロープははずれ，2 人とも何も得られない。

そこから数 km 離れたライプチヒ動物園の「ポンゴ・ランド」では，透明アクリル板の囲いのなかで同じ実験が行われている。ただし対象は幼児ではなく 2 頭のチンパンジーだ。うまくできたら，2 頭はそれぞれおいしい果物を手に入れられる。

研究者たちはこれらの実験によって，「ヒトという生物種がここまで成功したのはなぜか」という長年の謎を解こうとしている。ヒト（*Homo sapiens*）とチンパンジー（*Pan troglodytes*）はゲノムの 99%が共通だ。ではなぜ，人間は地球の隅々にまで居住範囲を広げ，エッフェル塔やジャンボジェット機，さらには水爆を作り出すことができたのか？　そして一方のチンパンジーはなぜ，依然として熱帯アフリカの深い森のなかで食物をあさっているのか？　チンパンジーの暮らしは，人類がこの霊長類との共通祖先から分岐した約 700 万年前と同じだ。

数十万年から数百万年に及ぶ進化の時間スケールで起こった出来事はみなそうだが，実際に何が起きたかについて科学者の意見が 1 つにまとまることは決してないかもしれない。かつては，人間だけが道具を作って使い，数やその他の表象を用いて推論ができるのだとみられていた。だが，ヒト以外の霊長類の能力に関する理解が深まるにつれ，この見方は覆った。適切に教えてやれば，チンパンジーも足し算ができ，パソコンを操作でき，くわえたタバコに火をつけられる。

人間とチンパンジーの行動がなぜ異なり，どれだけ違うのかという疑問は現在もなお議論の的だ。だが，マックス・プランク進化人類学研究所の支援のもとライプチヒで行われている上述の実験などによって，実に興味深い可能性が明らかになった。人間の認知機構が持つ，おそらく独特だが見逃されやすい側面が特定されたのだ。子どもは 1 歳の誕生日を迎える前から，母親や父親が考えていることを明敏に認識し始める（一部の心理学者が「9 カ月革命」と呼ぶ転換点だ）。親の視線を追ったり指さした先を見たりするのが，その表れだ。チンパンジーも仲間の考えていることをある程度は理解できるが，人間はその一歩先を行く。幼児も大人も，額を集めて相談し，共通の目的を達成するためにしなければならないことに集中する能力を持っている。大人と幼児が相手に向かってボールを転がし合うという単純な行動は，チンパンジーと比べたこのわずかな認知的利点のなせる業だ。

一部の心理学者と人類学者は，この“心の共有”が数十万年前に生じた重要な変化で，その後の人間の進化を形作ったのだろうと考えている。狩猟採集民の小集団が協力して働けるようになったことが，ついには一連の認知上の変化を引き起こし，言語の発達と世界各地への様々な文化の広がりにつながった。

ヒトの心の進化に関するこの説明は子どもとチンパンジーの研究から生まれた推論であり，疑問視する向きもある。だが，人間を特別な存在にしてい

この記事の読み方

記事の原題は“The “It” Factor”。ヒトとチンパンジーを違うものにしている決定的なファクターはなにか，それがこれ（“It”），といった意味。邦題はリード文の説明のほうを採用している。

記事のなかで紹介されているのは，チンパンジーと人間の子どもでの認知課題の比較実験。言ってみれば「知恵比べ」。これによって双方の認知能力の特殊性が明らかになる。チンパンジーと大きく異なるのは，相手の意図や心の状態を推測するという点である。記事では，人間どうしの shared intentionality（意図の共有／共有意図）こそが協力や共同作業を可能にし，さらには複雑な社会を作り上げることを可能にしたという論が展開されている。これに関連して，ダンバーの social brain hypothesis（社会脳仮説）も紹介されている。

ratchet は「つめ車」のこと。トマセロのいう ratchet effect（ラチェット効果）は，つめ車が段階的に進んでゆくように，改良が累積して進化することを指している。ほかの分野（たとえば経済学）にもラチェット効果と呼ばれるものがあるが，これとは意味が異なる。

る認知能力の起源について，最も広範な描像を提供しているといえるだろう。

ラチェット効果

マックス・プランク進化人類学研究所はヒトと類人猿の行動の違いを専門に研究する世界最大の施設を擁している。常に数十件の研究が行われ，研究者は2万人以上の子どもが登録されたデーターベースから被験者を選べるうえ，数km離れたライプチヒ動物園のヴォルフガング・ケーラー霊長類研究センターにいるチンパンジーやオランウータン，ボノボ，ゴリラといった類人猿を研究に利用できる。

この研究所の設立はいまから17年前，東西ドイツ再統一から7年後だった。設立にはドイツ人類学の汚点と，ナチスの人種差別的イデオロギーとの関連，特に人類学の学位を持つ医師メンゲレ（Josef Mengele）によるアウシュビッツでの身の毛のよだつ人体実験という負の歴史に向き合う必要があった。研究所の設立委員たちは，遺伝学や霊長類学，言語学などの研究グループリーダーにドイツ人以外の人材を採用した。

トマセロ（Michael Tomasello）はその1人だ。ひげをたくわえたこの長身の心理学者・霊長類学者は現在64歳。フロリダ半島のど真ん中にあるオレンジを産する小さな町で育った。幼児の言語習得の研究によってジョージア大学で学位を得た。彼が博士論文をまとめた1970年代，動物界におけるヒトの最も例外的な特徴は言語であるというのが，言語学者と心理学者の見方だった。

トマセロはこの博士論文で，自身の2歳弱の娘がどのように動詞を学習するかを記録した。“play play”や“ni ni”といった前言語の出現は，試行錯誤で言語要素をあれこれ試す傾向が幼児に自然に備わっていることを示している。この練習を通じて徐々に，より様式的な文法と構文の構造が獲得される。文法が何らかの形で脳に遺伝的に組み込まれていると主張するチョムスキー（Noam Chomsky）ら言語学者の考え方とは対照的だ。トマセロはこのような還元主義的説明に納得できなかった。「言語は非常に複雑なものであり，他の指と向かい合わせにできる親指が進化したのと同じ具合に生じることはありえない」という。

トマセロは言語の研究を通じて，文化と人類進化の関係についての考察を広げた。身体的形質に働く選択圧だけでは，ヒトとチンパンジーが分岐して以来の比較的短い進化史の間に複雑な道具や言語，数学，精緻な社会制度などが出現したことを説明できないと彼は考えた。ヒト以外の霊長類にはない生来の知的能力が私たちの祖先に生じ，それによって可能になった行動が，衣食を確保し過酷な環境下でも生きていける能力の獲得を大いに促進したに違いない。

トマセロは1980年代にエモリー大学の教授となり，同大学にあるヤーキス霊長類研究センターを利用して子どもとチンパンジーの行動を比較研究することで，この能力につながる手がかりを探した。その研究は1998年にマックス・プランク研究所に移ってからも続き，現在に至っている。

チンパンジーの学習を研究するなかで，彼らが互いを猿真似する仕方はヒトが他者を真似る仕方とは異なることにトマセロは気づいた。棒を使ってアリを巣から引き出しているチンパンジーを他のチンパンジーが真似ることはあるだろう。群れにいる別のチンパンジーが続いて同じことをするかもしれない。しかしトマセロがさらに詳しく観察した結果，チンパンジーは棒を「アリ釣り」に使えることを理解できてはいるが，アリ釣りに使えそうな何か別の技法を真似ることには無関心であることがうかがえた。より重要なことに，基本を学ぶだけで，手を加えて改良しようとする試みは見られない。

人間社会では対照的に，この種のイノベーションが顕著な特徴となっている。トマセロはこれを「ラチェット効果」と呼ぶ。人間は道具を改良してその知識を次世代に伝え，その人たちがさらに独自の改良を加える。こうしてラチェット（つめ車）が一段ずつ回るように，改良が徐々に積み重なっていく。そのようにして，マンモスを倒すために発明された石投げ装置が，何千年もの間に投石機からカタパルト，弾丸，ついには大陸間弾道ミサイルへと進化したのだ。

この文化的ラチェットは生物種としてのヒトの成功を大まかに説明できる一方で，別の疑問につながる。そうした知識を他者に伝えるのに必要となった知的プロセスとは何だったのか，という疑問だ。これに答えを出すには，数十万年前に人類の生理機能と行動に生じたと思われる変化について推測することから始めねばならない。英オックスフォード大学の人類学者ダンバー（Robin Dunbar）が提唱した「社会脳仮説」は，脳が大きくなるにつれて人間集団のサイズと文化的複雑さが増したと考える。40 万年前には，現生人類の直接の先祖とみられるホモ・ハイデルベルゲンシス（*Homo heidelbergensis*）がすでに私たちとほぼ同じ大きさの脳を持っていたことがわかっている。

大きな脳を持ち，より多くの人口を養う必要に直面した初期人類は，獲物を追跡して裏をかくために注意深い作戦を練り始めたのだろうとトマセロは考えている。この環境が，協力に対する強い選択圧となった。獲物を追い詰めるために入念に役割分担を決めたのに，役目を果たさずチームプレーをぶち壊したメンバーは，その後の狩りから排除されて厳しい現実に直面しただろう。うまく協力できないメンバーは仲間から「二度とご免だ」と見限られたとトマセロは指摘する。この見方に立つと，初期人類と現代人とを分けたのは，優れて社会的な生活を行うための進化的適応だった。

Gary Stix
SCIENTIFIC AMERICAN 誌のシニアライター。

The Attention Economy

SNSがしょうもない
情報であふれる
メカニズム

E. メンツァー
（米インディアナ大学）

T. ヒルズ
（英ウォーリック大学）

アルゴリズムや情報操作者が
どのように人の認知の脆弱性につけこんでいるかを理解すれば
それに対抗する方策が見えてくる

KEY CONCEPTS

ネット情報の洪水が増幅する認知バイアス

- 人間は誰もみな認知バイアスを抱えている。信頼している仲間からの情報を採用し，リスクに関する情報に注意を払い，自分の考え方に合致する証拠を偏重する。
- 現代の技術とオンライン情報の洪水はこのバイアスを有害な形で増幅している。認知の脆弱性につけこんだ誤情報キャンペーンも現実化している。
- これらを理解することが，対抗策を考えるうえで喫緊の課題だ。

日経サイエンス 2021年8月号，SCIENTIFIC AMERICAN December 2020

Consider Andy, who is worried about contracting COVID-19. Unable to read all the articles he sees on it, he relies on trusted friends for tips. When one opines on Facebook that pandemic fears are overblown, Andy dismisses the idea at first. But then the hotel where he works closes its doors, and with his job at risk, Andy starts wondering how serious the threat from the new virus really is. No one he knows has died, after all. A colleague posts an article about the COVID "scare" having been created by Big Pharma in collusion with corrupt politicians, which jibes with Andy's distrust of government. His Web search quickly takes him to articles claiming that COVID-19 is no worse than the flu. Andy joins an online group of people who have been or fear being laid off and soon finds himself asking, like many of them, "What pandemic?" When he learns that several of his new friends are planning to attend a rally demanding an end to lockdowns, he decides to join them. Almost no one at the massive protest, including him, wears a mask. When his sister asks about the rally, Andy shares the conviction that has now become part of his identity: COVID is a hoax.

This example illustrates a minefield of cognitive biases. We prefer information from people we trust, our in-group. We pay attention to and are more likely to share information about risks—for Andy, the risk of losing his job. We search for and remember things that fit well with what we already know and understand. These biases are products of our evolutionary past, and for tens of thousands of years, they served us well. People who behaved in accordance with them—for example, by staying away from the overgrown pond bank where someone said there was a viper—were more likely to survive than those who did not.

Modern technologies are amplifying these biases in harmful ways, however. Search engines direct Andy to sites that inflame his suspicions, and social media connects him with like-minded people, feeding his fears.

Vocabulary

［タイトル］attention economy アテンションエコノミー（関心経済）
▶この記事の読み方

contract 罹患する，病気にかかる
tip 情報，アドバイス
opine 考えを述べる
overblown 大げさな
dismiss 退ける，取り合わない
close its doors 休業する，営業を停止する
after all 結局のところ，何しろ〜なのだから
colleague 同僚
COVID "scare" 「コロナ騒ぎ」
Big Pharma 医薬品大手
in collusion with 〜と結託（共謀）して
corrupt 腐敗した，堕落した，汚職の
jibe with 〜と一致する
distrust 不信
no worse than 〜と変わりない
flu インフルエンザ
lay off 一時解雇する
rally 集会
hoax でっち上げ

minefield 地雷原
cognitive bias 認知バイアス
in-group 内集団
attention 関心，注意
evolutionary past 進化の歴史，これまでの進化
overgrown 草の生い茂った
pond bank 池の土手
viper 毒ヘビ

amplify 増幅する
direct 誘導する
inflame 火をつける，たきつける
suspicion 疑念
like-minded 同じ考えを持った
feed （不安を）あおる

Making matters worse, bots—automated social media accounts that impersonate humans—enable misguided or malevolent actors to take advantage of his vulnerabilities.

Compounding the problem is the proliferation of online information. Viewing and producing blogs, videos, tweets and other units of information called memes has become so cheap and easy that the information marketplace is inundated. Unable to process all this material, we let our cognitive biases decide what we should pay attention to. These mental shortcuts influence which information we search for, comprehend, remember and repeat to a harmful extent.

The need to understand these cognitive vulnerabilities and how algorithms use or manipulate them has become urgent. At the University of Warwick in England and at Indiana University Bloomington's Observatory on Social Media (OSoMe, pronounced "awesome"), our teams are using cognitive experiments, simulations, data mining and artificial intelligence to comprehend the cognitive vulnerabilities of social media users. Insights from psychological studies on the evolution of information conducted at Warwick inform the computer models developed at Indiana, and vice versa. We are also developing analytical and machine-learning aids to fight social media manipulation. Some of these tools are already being used by journalists, civil-society organizations and individuals to detect inauthentic actors, map the spread of false narratives and foster news literacy.

Information Overload

The glut of information has generated intense competition for people's attention. As Nobel Prize–winning economist and psychologist Herbert A. Simon noted, "What information consumes is rather obvious: it consumes the attention of its recipients." One of the first consequences of the so-called attention economy is the

Vocabulary

bot ボット
impersonate (人に)なりすます, (人を)装う
misguided 見当違いの
malevolent 悪意のある
actor 人物, 関係者
take advantage of ～につけこむ
vulnerability 脆弱性

compound さらに悪化させる
proliferation 急増
meme ミーム
inundated 氾濫状態の
material 情報
shortcut 手っ取り早い方法, 便法
comprehend 把握する, 理解する
to a harmful extent 有害なまでに

cognitive vulnerability 認知の脆弱性
▶この記事の読み方
urgent 喫緊の
data mining データマイニング
artificial intelligence 人工知能
insight 洞察, 知見
evolution 進化
and vice versa 逆もまた然り
analytical and machine-learning aids 解析ツールや機械学習ツール
manipulation (情報)操作
civil-society organization 市民社会組織
inauthentic 偽の
false narrative 虚偽の物語
foster 育成する

overload 過負荷, 過剰供給, 氾濫
glut 供給過剰
recipient 受け取る人
consequence 結果

loss of high-quality information. The OSoMe team demonstrated this result with a set of simple simulations. It represented users of social media such as Andy, called agents, as nodes in a network of online acquaintances. At each time step in the simulation, an agent may either create a meme or reshare one that he or she sees in a news feed. To mimic limited attention, agents are allowed to view only a certain number of items near the top of their news feeds.

Vocabulary

represent 表現する
agent 主体(エージェント)
node ノード
acquaintance 知り合い
time step タイムステップ
reshare 再シェアする
mimic 模擬する

Running this simulation over many time steps, Lilian Weng of OSoMe found that as agents' attention became increasingly limited, the propagation of memes came to reflect the power-law distribution of actual social media: the probability that a meme would be shared a given number of times was roughly an inverse power of that number. For example, the likelihood of a meme being shared three times was approximately nine times less than that of its being shared once.

propagation 拡散
power-law distribution べき乗則分布
probability 確率
inverse power 逆べき
likelihood 可能性, 確率

This winner-take-all popularity pattern of memes, in which most are barely noticed while a few spread widely, could not be explained by some of them being more catchy or somehow more valuable: the memes in this simulated world had no intrinsic quality. Virality resulted purely from the statistical consequences of information proliferation in a social network of agents with limited attention. Even when agents preferentially shared memes of higher quality, researcher Xiaoyan Qiu, then at OSoMe, observed little improvement in the overall quality of those shared the most. Our models revealed that even when we want to see and share high-quality information, our inability to view everything in our news feeds inevitably leads us to share things that are partly or completely untrue.

winner-take-all 勝者総取り型の
catchy 魅力的な
intrinsic 固有の
virality バイラリティー(拡散性)
▶この記事の読み方
result 生じる
preferentially 優先的に
inevitably 必然的に

Cognitive biases greatly worsen the problem. In a set of groundbreaking studies in 1932, psychologist Frederic Bartlett told volunteers a Native American legend about a young man who hears war cries and, pursuing

groundbreaking 画期的な
war cry ときの声

them, enters a dreamlike battle that eventually leads to his real death. Bartlett asked the volunteers, who were non-Native, to recall the rather confusing story at increasing intervals, from minutes to years later. He found that as time passed, the rememberers tended to distort the tale's culturally unfamiliar parts such that they were either lost to memory or transformed into more familiar things. We now know that our minds do this all the time: they adjust our understanding of new information so that it fits in with what we already know. One consequence of this so-called confirmation bias is that people often seek out, recall and understand information that best confirms what they already believe.

This tendency is extremely difficult to correct. Experiments consistently show that even when people encounter balanced information containing views from differing perspectives, they tend to find supporting evidence for what they already believe. And when people with divergent beliefs about emotionally charged issues such as climate change are shown the same information on these topics, they become even more committed to their original positions.

Making matters worse, search engines and social media platforms provide personalized recommendations based on the vast amounts of data they have about users' past preferences. They prioritize information in our feeds that we are most likely to agree with—no matter how fringe—and shield us from information that might change our minds. This makes us easy targets for polarization. Nir Grinberg and his co-workers at Northeastern University recently showed that conservatives in the U.S. are more receptive to misinformation. But our own analysis of consumption of low-quality information on Twitter shows that the vulnerability applies to both sides of the political spectrum, and no one can fully avoid it. Even our ability to detect online manipulation is affected by our political

Vocabulary

distort 歪める
confirmation bias 確証バイアス
▶この記事の読み方

supporting 裏づけとなるような
divergent 異なる
charged 熱を帯びた
committed 肩入れする，傾倒する

personalized recommendation 各個人に向けた「お薦め」
preference 選好
prioritize 優先表示する
fringe 主流から外れた
shield 遮断する
polarization 二極分化
conservatives 保守派
receptive 受け入れやすい
misinformation 誤情報
apply 当てはまる
political spectrum （保守からリベラルまで全範囲にわたる）政治的立場

bias, though not symmetrically: Republican users are more likely to mistake bots promoting conservative ideas for humans, whereas Democrats are more likely to mistake conservative human users for bots.

Vocabulary

Republican 共和党支持の
mistake A for B AをBと間違える，思い違いする
Democrats 民主党支持者

COVID-19 の感染を心配しているアンディを考えよう。目にした記事すべてを読むのは無理なので，信頼できる友人たちの話を頼りにしている。ある友達がフェイスブックでパンデミックの危険が誇張されていると述べたとき，アンディは最初はそれに取り合わなかった。だが勤め先のホテルが営業を停止して失業の恐れが生じると，新型コロナの脅威が果たしてどれほど深刻なのか疑い始めた。何しろ，知り合いでコロナで死んだ人は 1 人もいない。そんなとき，ある同僚が，医薬品大手と汚職政治家たちが共謀して「コロナ騒ぎ」を作り上げたとする記事を投稿し，これが政府に対するアンディの不信と一致する。彼がネットを検索すると，COVID-19 はインフルエンザと変わらないと主張する記事がすぐに見つかった。アンディはコロナで一時解雇された人やその不安を抱える人たちのオンライングループに加わり，間もなく彼らと同様に「どこがパンデミックなんだ？」と声を上げるようになる。新たにできた友達の数人がロックダウン終結を求める集会に参加する予定を知り，彼も参加を決める。この大規模抗議行動に加わった人は彼を含めほぼ全員がマスクを着用しなかった。帰宅して妹に集会のことを尋ねられたアンディは，いまや自分のアイデンティティーの一部となった確信を妹と共有する。「COVID はでっち上げだ」。

この例は認知バイアスの地雷原を示している。私たちはみな，自分が信頼している人たちからの情報，つまり仲間内である「内集団」からの情報を好んで採用する。また，リスクに関する情報に注意を払い，それを共有する傾向がある。アンディの場合は失業のリスクだ。そして，すでに知って理解している事柄と合致する事柄を探して記憶する。これらのバイアスはこれまでの進化の産物であり，何万年もの間，役に立ってきた。これらに従って行動した人（例えば毒ヘビがいると誰かが言った池のほとりの茂みを避けた人たち）は，そうしなかった人よりも生き延びる可能性が高くなった。

しかし，現代の技術はこれらのバイアスを有害な形で増幅している。検索エンジンはアンディの疑念をたきつけるサイトに彼を誘導し，ソーシャルメディアは彼を同様の考えを持つ人たちと結びつけて不安をあおる。さらに悪いことに，ボット（人間を装った自動 SNS アカウント）は，悪意ある者がアンディの脆弱性につけこむことを可能にする。

この問題をさらにひどくしているのはオンライン情報の急増だ。ブログや動画，ツイートなどの情報単位（「ミーム」と呼ばれる）を非常に安く簡単に閲覧・作成できるようになったため，日常世界にそうした情報があふれている。すべてを処理するのは無理なので，私たちは何に注目すべきかを認知バイアスに任せて決める。この心的便法は，私たちがどの情報を検索・理解・記憶して有害なまでに反復するかに影響を与えている。

これらの認知的脆弱性と，いかにアルゴリズムがそれにつけこんでいるかを理解することが，いまや喫緊の課題となっている。私たち著者のチームは英ウォーリック大学と米インディアナ大学ブルーミントン校ソーシャルメディア観測所（OSoMe，オーサム）において，認知実験とシミュレーション，データマイニング，人工知能を用いてSNSユーザーの認知的脆弱性を把握しようとしている。ウォーリック大学で行った情報の進化に関する心理学研究からの知見をインディアナ大学で開発するコンピューターモデルに反映し，逆にモデルの結果を心理学研究に生かしている。また，ソーシャルメディアの情報操作に対抗するための解析ツールや機械学習ツールも開発している。すでに一部のツールはジャーナリストや市民社会組織，個人によって，ボットなど偽物の発見や，虚偽の物語が拡散する状況の地図化，ニュースリテラシーの育成に利用されている。

氾濫する情報

情報過多は人々の関心を奪い合う競争を生んだ。ノーベル賞経済学者で心理学者でもあるサイモン（Herbert A. Simon）が指摘したように，「情報の豊かさは注意の貧困をもたらす」。いわゆるアテンションエコノミー（関心・注意を消費する経済）の初期の結果の1つは，良質の情報の喪失だ。OSoMeのチームは一連の簡単なシミュレーションによってこれを実証した。SNSを利用しているアンディのような主体（エージェント）をオンラインの知り合いネットワークを構成するノードとして表現し，各タイムステップごとに1人のエージェントが1つのミームを作成するか，自分のニュースフィードで見たミームのうち1つを再シェアするというシミュレーションだ。関心が限られている状態を模擬するため，各エージェントはニュース配信の上位にある一定数の項目しか閲覧できないとした。

OSoMe のウェン（Lilian Weng）はこのシミュレーションを多くのタイムステップにわたって実行し，エージェントの関心が制限されるほど，ミームの拡散が実際の SNS に見られる「べき乗則分布」を反映するようになることを発見した。ミームが一定回数シェアされる確率は，その回数の 2 乗にほぼ反比例して減少した。例えば，あるミームが 3 回シェアされる確率は，1 回シェアされる確率の約 1/9 だ。

大部分のミームはほとんど注目されずごく一部が広まる勝者総取り型のこの人気パターンは，一部のミームがより魅力的だとか何らかの価値があるという理由では説明できない。このシミュレーションにおけるミームは固有の質など持っていないからだ。このバイラリティー（拡散性）は，関心が限られたエージェントで構成されたソーシャルネットにおいて情報が広がる純粋に統計的な結果か

この記事の読み方

行動経済学は，人間の判断や意思決定の非合理性をあつかう心理学と経済学のハイブリッドの分野である。記事は，行動経済学の観点から，人間の cognitive vulnerabilities（認知の脆弱性）をとりあげている。

記事の邦題はくだけているが，原題は “The Attention Economy”。attention は心理学では「注意」と訳すが，行動経済学ではもっと広く，関心や注目の程度ととらえている。attention economy は「関心経済」や「アテンションエコノミー」と訳される。

掲載文では，なぜ仲間内，すなわち in-group（内集団）では特定の情報が注目され，その情報が拡散し信じられてしまうのかを認知バイアスの 1 つ，confirmation bias（確証バイアス）の点から解説している。強調されているのは，ネットの情報操作がそうした認知バイアスを利用する形で行われているという点である。文中に出てくる virality（バイラリティー）はネット用語。viral（ウイルスの）の名詞形で，ウイルスのような伝染性・拡散性のことを指している。

記事の後半では，エコーチェンバー効果が解説されたあと，ネットの情報操作にどう対処すればよいかが論じられている。

ら生じた。当時 OSoMe にいたチウ（Xiaoyan Qiu）は，エージェントが良質のミームを優先的にシェアするようにシミュレーションの設定を変えても，最も多くシェアされたミームの質は総じてほとんど向上しないことを見いだした。人々が質の高い情報を得てシェアしたいと思っていても，ニュース配信すべてに目を通すことができないために，部分的あるいは完全に間違った情報のシェアに必然的につながってしまうことが明らかになった。

認知バイアスはこの問題を大幅に悪化させる。心理学者のバートレット（Frederic Bartlett）は 1932 年の画期的な研究で，被験者にアメリカ先住民の伝説を聞かせる実験をした。若い男が雄叫びを聞いて追っていくと幻想的な戦闘が始まり，ついには自分が死んでしまう話だ。バートレットは少々わかりにくいこの物語を先住民ではない被験者に聞いてもらい，その数分後，数日後というように間隔を増しながら数年後まで，異なる時点で物語を思い出してもらった。この結果，時間がたつにつれ，物語のうち文化的に馴染みの薄い部分が忘れられたり身近な事柄に置き換えられるなどして，物語が歪められる傾向が見いだされた。現在では，これが人の心の常であることがわかっている。人は新たな情報に関する理解を調節して，自分がすでに知っていることに適合させるのだ。この「確証バイアス」の結果，人はたいてい，自分がすでに信じていることを最もよく裏づける情報を見つけ，思い出し，理解する。

この傾向を正すのは極めて難しい。人は様々な視点の見解を含む偏りのない情報に接しても，すでに信じ込んでいる事柄を裏づけるような証拠を見つける傾向があることが，実験から一貫して示されている。そして，例えば気候変動問題など感情的な色彩を帯びた問題について異なる信念を持っている人々がそのテーマについて同じ情報を提示された場合，自分が持っていたもともとの立場にいっそう固執するようになる。

さらに悪いことに，検索エンジンや SNS はユーザーの過去の選好について集めた膨大なデータに基づいて，各個人に向けた「お薦め」を提示する。ユーザーが賛同する可能性の最も高い情報を（いかに主流から外れたものであっても），ニュースフィードの上位に優先表示し，考え方を変えるきっかけとなるような情報を遮断しているのだ。これは私たちを二極分化の容易な標的にしている。ノースイースタン大学のグリンバーグ（Nir Grinberg）らは最近，米国の保守派は誤情報を受け入れやすいことを示した。だが，私たちがツイッター上の質の低い情報の消費を調べた別の解析では，この脆弱性は政治的立場の左右両サイドに当てはまり，完全に免れることのできる人はいない。オンライン情報操作を検知する能力さえも，政治的バイアスの影響を受ける。ただしこれは非対称的で，共和党支持のユーザーは保守的な考えを後押しするボットを人間と間違えがちなのに対し，民主党支持のユーザーは保守的な人間のユーザーをボットと間違える傾向が強い。

Filippo Menczer ／ Thomas Hill
メンツァーは米インディアナ大学ブルーミントン校ソーシャルメディア観測所（OSoMe）の所長で，情報・コンピューター科学の卓越教授。偽情報の拡散を研究，ソーシャルメディアの操作に対抗するツールを開発している。ヒルズは英ウォーリック大学の心理学教授で行動科学・データ科学の修士コースの責任者。研究テーマは知性の進化と情報。

An Invisible Epidemic

コロナ禍で増えた心の病
モラルインジャリー

E. スヴォボダ
（サイエンスライター）

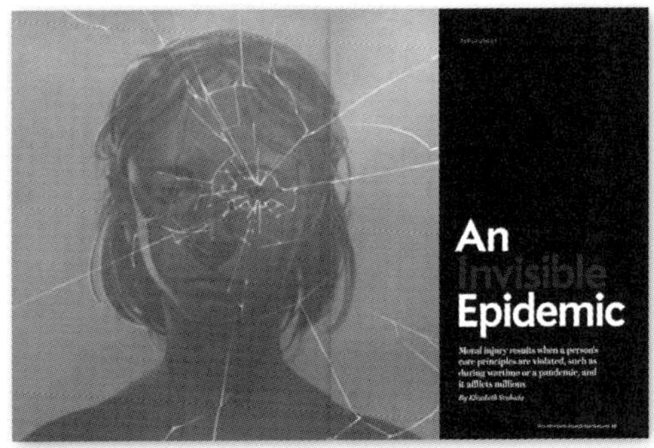

さながら戦場のようなパンデミックの医療現場では
自身の価値観や良心に反する行動を取るしかない状況に追い込まれ
何百万人もの人々が精神的に深い傷を負って苦しんでいる

KEY CONCEPTS

倫理観に反する行動が生むトラウマ

- ■パンデミックの救急現場などでは，医療従事者が自身の価値観や倫理観に反する行動を取るしかない状況に追い込まれ，ある種のトラウマを負う人が増えている。
- ■モラルインジャリーと呼ばれる心の病で，うつになったり，自殺の衝動に駆られたりする恐れが高まる可能性が指摘されている。
- ■モラルインジャリー向けに考案されたセラピーでは，問題を道徳的な観点から整理することに重点を置き，臨床研究で治療の有効性が確認されつつある。

日経サイエンス 2023年4月号，SCIENTIFIC AMERICAN December 2022

In early 2021 emergency room physician Torree McGowan hoped the worst of the pandemic was behind her. She and her colleagues had adapted to the COVID-causing virus, donning layers of protection before seeing each patient, but they'd managed to keep things running smoothly. The central Oregon region where McGowan lived—a high desert plateau ringed by snow-capped mountains—had largely escaped the first COVID waves that slammed areas such as New York City.

Then the virus's Delta variant hit central Oregon with exponential fury, and the delicate balance McGowan had maintained came crashing down. Suddenly, COVID patients were streaming into the ERs at the hospitals where she worked, and she had to tell many patients she was powerless to help them because the few drugs she had didn't work in late stages of the disease. "That feels really terrible," McGowan says. "That's not what any of us signed up for."

It wasn't just COVID patients McGowan couldn't help. It was also everyone else. People still approached a health-care emergency with the expectation that they were going to be taken care of right away. But in the midst of the surge, there were no beds. "And I don't have a helicopter that can fly you between my hospital and the next hospital," she says, "because they're all full." A patient with suspected colon cancer showed up bleeding in the ER, and McGowan's inner impulses screamed that she needed to admit the woman immediately for testing. But because there were no beds left, she had to send the patient home instead.

The need to abandon her own standards and watch people suffer and die was hard enough for McGowan. Just as disorienting, though, was the sense that more and more patients no longer cared what happened to her or anyone else. She had assumed she and her patients played

Vocabulary

［タイトル］ **invisible** 見えない
▶この記事の読み方

epidemic 伝染病, 疫病
emergency room physician 救急医
be behind someone 脱した, 過ぎ去った
colleague 同僚
adapt 対応を図る, 対策を講じる
don 着用する
protection 防護服
see 診察する
plateau 台地, 高原
ring 取り囲む
slam 席巻する, 襲う

Delta variant デルタ株
exponential fury 急拡大する猛威
crash down 崩れ去る
ER 緊急救命室, 緊急治療室
work 効く
sign up （署名して）加わる, 契約する

health-care emergency 医療緊急事態
right away すぐに
in the midst of ～の真っ最中
surge （パンデミックの）大波
full 満床
suspected colon cancer 結腸がんの疑いのある
bleed 出血する
inner impulse 抑えきれない思い
admit 入院させる

abandon 断念する
disorienting 当惑させる, 途方に暮れさせる
care 気にかける, 思いやりを示す
assume 当然と思う, 思い込む

by the same basic rules—that she would try her utmost to help them get better and that they would support her or at least treat her humanely.

But as the virus extended its reach, those relationships broke down. Unvaccinated COVID patients walked into the exam room maskless, against hospital policy. They cursed her out for telling them they had the virus. "I have heard so many people say, 'I don't care if I make someone sick and kill them,'" McGowan says. Their ruthlessness simultaneously terrified and enraged her—not least because she had an immunocompromised husband at home. "Every month I do hours and hours of continuing education," McGowan says. "Every patient that I've ever made a mistake on, I can tell you every bit about that. And the thought that people are so callous with a life, when I place so much value on somebody's life—it's a lot to carry."

Moral injury is a specific trauma that arises when people face situations that deeply violate their conscience or threaten their core values. Those who grapple with it, such as McGowan, can struggle with guilt, anger and a consuming sense that they can't forgive themselves or others.

The condition affects millions across many roles. In an atmosphere of rationed care, doctors must admit a few patients and turn many away. Soldiers kill civilians to complete assigned missions. Veterinarians must put animals down when no one steps up to adopt them.

The trauma is far more widespread and devastating than most people realize. "It's really clear to us that it is all over the place," says psychiatrist Wendy Dean, president and co-founder of the nonprofit Moral Injury of Healthcare in Carlisle, Pa. "It's social workers, educators, lawyers." Survey studies in the U.S. report that more than half of K–12 professionals, including teachers, moderately

Vocabulary

utmost 全力
humanely 人間的な思いやりを持って

unvaccinated ワクチン未接種の
curse someone out （人に）罵詈雑言を浴びせる
ruthlessness 非情さ，冷酷さ
enrage 激怒させる
not least とりわけ
immunocompromised 免疫不全の
callous 冷淡な，無感覚な
when 〜というのに，〜であるのに
a lot to carry 背負うのが大変，耐えられない

moral injury モラルインジャリー（道徳的負傷）
▶この記事の読み方
trauma トラウマ
conscience 良心
threaten 脅かす
core values 核となる価値観
grapple with 向き合う，取り組む
struggle with 〜と格闘（苦闘）する
guilt 罪悪感
consuming sense 痛切な感覚

rationed 配給制の，制限された
turn someone away 門前払いする
civilian 一般市民
complete 完遂する
assigned 与えられた
veterinarian 獣医
put animals down 動物を殺処分する
step up to 進んで〜する，〜する責任を引き受ける
adopt （動物を）引き取る

devastating 破壊的な，深刻な
psychiatrist 精神科医

or strongly agree that they have faced morally injurious situations involving others. Similar studies in Europe show that about half of physicians have been exposed to potentially morally injurious events at high levels.

Even these figures may be artificially low, given scant public awareness of moral injury: many people do not yet have the vocabulary to describe what is happening to them. Whatever the exact numbers, the mental health effects are vast. In a King's College London meta-analysis that surveyed 13 studies, moral injury predicted higher rates of depression and suicidal impulses.

When COVID swept the planet, the moral injury crisis became more pressing as ethically wrenching dilemmas became the new normal—not just for health-care workers but for others in frontline roles. Store employees had to risk their own safety and that of vulnerable family members to make a living. Lawyers often could not meet clients in person, making it nearly impossible to represent those clients adequately. In such situations, "no matter how hard you work, you're always going to be falling short," says California public defender Jenny Andrews.

Although moral injury doesn't yet have its own listing in diagnostic manuals, there is a growing consensus that it is a condition that is distinct from depression or post-traumatic stress disorder (PTSD). This consensus has given rise to treatments that aim to help people resolve long-standing ethical traumas. These treatments—vital additions to a broad range of trauma therapies—encourage people to face moral conflicts head-on rather than blotting them out or explaining them away, and they emphasize the importance of community support in long-term recovery. In some cases, therapy clients even create plans to make amends for harms committed.

Vocabulary

K–12 幼稚園から12年生(高校3年生)までの教育課程
moderately 中程度に
involve ～を巻き込む，～にまつわる(からむ)
exposed さらされる，直面する

artificially 人為的に，不自然に
scant 不十分な，足りない
public awareness 社会の認識
vast 甚大な
meta-analysis メタ解析
predict 予示する
depression うつ病，うつ状態
suicidal impulse 自殺衝動

sweep 席巻する
pressing 切迫した
ethically wrenching 道徳的な苦悩を伴う
new normal 新たな日常
frontline 最前線の，現場の
vulnerable 感染リスクの高い
in person 対面で
fall short 目標に届かない，十分な役目を果たせない
public defender 公選弁護人

listing 記載
diagnostic manual 診断マニュアル
post-traumatic stress disorder 心的外傷後ストレス障害
given rise to ～につながる
long-standing 積年の，長年の
conflict 葛藤
head-on 真正面から
blot out 消し去る
explain away 説明によって解消する
make amends for ～の償いをする
harms committed 自分が与えた害

Even if moral injury research is a young and growing field, scientists and clinicians already agree that a key step toward healing for morally injured people—whether in therapy or not—has to do with grasping the true nature of what they're facing. They're not hopeless, "bad seeds" or uniquely irredeemable. They may not fit the criteria for PTSD or another mental illness. Instead they're suffering from a severe disconnect between the moral principles they live by and the reality of what is happening or has happened. In moral injury, "that sense of who you are as a person has been brought into question," Dean says. "We have a lot of people saying, 'This is the language I've been looking for for the past 20 years.'"

Vocabulary

clinician 臨床医
have to do with ～と関係がある
grasp 理解する
bad seed 問題児
uniquely 比類なく
irredeemable 矯正できない，救いようがない
criteria（単 **criterion**）基準
instead むしろ
disconnect 食い違い，乖離
live by ～に従って生きる，生きるよすがとしている

Ancient Origins

Although VA psychiatrist Jonathan Shay coined the term "moral injury" in the 1990s, the phenomenon predates its naming by millennia. In the ancient Greek epic The Iliad, the hero Achilles loses his best friend Patroclus in battle and then inwardly tortures himself because he failed to shield Patroclus from harm. When world wars broke out in the 20th century, people labeled as "battle fatigued" the returning soldiers who bore mental scars. In reality, many of them were tortured not by shell shock but by wartime deeds they felt too ashamed to recount. In the 1980s University of Nebraska Medical Center ethicist Andrew Jameton observed that this kind of moral distress was not confined to the military realm. It often "arises when one knows the right thing to do," he wrote, "but constraints make it nearly impossible to pursue the right course of action."

VA 退役軍人省
predate ～より前から存在する
millennia 数千年
epic 叙事詩
inwardly 心の中で
torture oneself 自分を責め苛む
battle fatigued 戦闘疲労
scar 傷痕，傷
shell shock 砲弾ショック
deed 行為
ashamed 恥ずかしい
recount 詳しく話す
ethicist 倫理学者
distress 苦悩
confined 限られる
realm 分野
constraint 制約

What spurred the first rigorous study of moral injury, however, was the multitude of U.S. soldiers struggling after serving in wars in Vietnam, Iraq and Afghanistan. Psychologist Brett Litz of the Veterans Affairs Boston Healthcare System saw quite a few vets of these conflicts who weren't responding well to counseling after their

spur 拍車をかける
rigorous 厳密な
multitude 数の多さ
Veterans Affairs 退役軍人省の
quite a few かなりの数の，相当多くの
vet（**veteran**）兵役経験者

deployments ended. They seemed to be stuck in stagnant grief over acts they'd committed, such as killing civilians in war zones. They reminded Litz of one of his past therapists who'd seemed oddly detached, never mentally present in the room. Afterward Litz found out why. "Probably months before I went to him, he had opened his car door, and he killed a child who was just biking down the road," Litz says. "He was as broken as can be. I witnessed firsthand what that was."

In long conversations with veterans, Litz grew convinced he was witnessing a condition that was different from PTSD and depression. PTSD typically takes root when someone's life or safety is threatened. But much of the lingering trauma Litz saw in vets had nothing to do with direct personal threat. It was related to mounting guilt and hopelessness, "the totality of the inhumanity, the lack of meaning and the participation in grotesque war things," he says. "They were pariahs—or felt that way, at least."

Building on Shay's earlier work, Litz resolved to develop a working concept of moral injury so that researchers could study it in depth and figure out how best to treat it. "I thought, 'This is going to affect our culture, and there are going to be broad impacts,'" he says. "We needed to bring science to bear. We needed to define the terms."

To that end, Litz and his colleagues published a comprehensive paper on moral injury in 2009, outlining common moral struggles veterans were facing and proposing a treatment approach that involved making personally meaningful reparations for harm done. He noted, too, that not all "potentially morally injurious events" cause moral injury. If you kill someone, and you feel totally justified in having done so, you may not experience moral injury at all. Moral injury tends to turn up when you have a vision of the world as fundamentally fair and good and something you've done or witnessed destroys that vision.

Vocabulary

deployment (軍隊への)配属
stuck in ～から抜け出せない
stagnant grief とめどない悲しみ, 悲嘆の沼
oddly 妙に
detached 超然とした, よそよそしい
never mentally present 心ここにあらず
go to (医者など)にかかる, ～に診てもらう
bike 自転車で走る
firsthand じかに, 自分の目で

convinced 確信して
take root 根づく
lingering 長引く
have nothing to do with ～とは関係がない
threat 脅威
mounting 高まる, 積み重なる
totality 総体
pariah 社会ののけ者

build on ～を踏まえて, ～をもとに
resolve 決意する
in depth 深く掘り下げて, 綿密に
bring science to bear 科学を活用する

to that end その目的に向けて
comprehensive 包括的な
involve 伴う
reparation 償い
potentially morally injurious events モラルインジャリーを引き起こす可能性のある出来事
turn up 姿を現す
fundamentally 基本的に

Litz's paper soon caught the attention of Rita Nakashima Brock, then a visiting scholar at Starr King School for the Ministry in California. A theologian and antiwar activist, Brock was preparing to convene the Truth Commission on Conscience in War, an event where returned soldiers would testify about the moral impact of engaging in battle.

Brock's antiwar activism had personal roots. After her father, a U.S. Army medic, returned from Vietnam, he withdrew from his family. When he did speak to his loved ones, he lashed out with an escalating rage. "My dad was so different that I didn't even want to be at home anymore," she says. After Brock's father died, she pieced together more of his story with a cousin's help. He had worked with a guide while deployed, a young Vietnamese woman who was later tortured and killed. He was horrified at what had happened—and likely also racked with guilt because he knew his ties to the guide could have put her in danger.

As soon as Brock saw Litz's moral injury paper, something clicked. "When my colleague and I read it, we said, 'Oh, my God, this is what the whole thing is about,'" she recalls. "We sent it to everybody testifying and said, 'Read this.'"

Vocabulary

visiting 客員
School for the Ministry 神学校
theologian 神学者
convene 開催する
testify 証言する

medic 衛生兵
withdraw 退く，距離を置く
lash out 食ってかかる
rage 怒り
different 人が変わって
piece together （断片をつなぎ合わせて）明らかにする
torture 拷問する
horrified 恐れおののく
racked with ～にひどく苛まれる

click ひらめく

2021年のはじめ，救急医のマクガワン（Torree McGowan）は，パンデミックの最悪の時期がこのまま過ぎ去るものと思っていた。同僚とともに新型コロナウイルスへの対策を講じ，患者を診る前には防護服を重ね着していたが，なんとか円滑に対処していた。マクガワンの住むオレゴン州中部は，雪を頂く山々に囲まれた砂漠の高原地帯で，ニューヨークなどの都市を襲った新型コロナウイルス感染症（COVID-19）の流行をおおむね回避していた。

ところが新型コロナウイルスのデルタ株がオレゴン州中部で急拡大すると，マクガワンらの努力で維持されていた微妙なバランスが崩れた。突如としてCOVIDの患者が病院の救急治療室に押し寄せた。手持ちの薬は少なく，それも重症者には効果がないため，助けることができないと多くの患者に告げなければならなかった。「本当に辛かった」とマクガワンは言う。「誰もこんなことを言うために医師になったわけではないのに」。

マクガワンが助けられなかったのはCOVIDの患者だけでない。ほかの病気や事故による救急患者も同様だった。人々はこれまで通り，すぐに救急対応してもらえるものと思って病院を頼った。しかし，パンデミックの大波の真っ最中は空きベッドがなかった。「うちの病院から別の病院に患者をヘリコプターで運ぶこともできなかった」と彼女は言う。「どこも満床だったから」。大腸がんが疑われる患者が出血して救急治療室にやってきた。マクガワンは，この女性をすぐに入院させて検査しなければならないと心の中で叫んでいた。しかし，空きベッドがない以上，患者を家に帰すしかなかった。

すべきことができないまま，患者が苦しみ，亡くなっていくのを目の当たりにするのはマクガワンにとって耐えがたかった。しかし，同時に頭を混乱させたのは，彼女のような医療従事者にも他の患者にも思いやりを示さない患者がどんどん増えつつあるという実感だった。彼女は，医師と患者は同じ規範に従って行動するものと考えていた。つまり自分は患者の治療に最善を尽くし，患者はそれに応え，少なくとも人として医療従事者を尊重するものと思っていた。

しかし，ウイルスが蔓延するにつれ，そうした関係は崩れ去った。ワクチン未接種の患者が，病院の方針を守らずマスクなしで診察室に入ってきた。新型コロナに感染していることを告げると，彼らは彼女に暴言を吐いた。「誰に感染させようが，誰かが死のうが，知ったことじゃない」と言う人がたくさんいたとマクガワンは話す。その冷酷さに彼女は恐怖と怒りを感じた。免疫不全の夫が家にいたからなおさらだった。「来る日も来る日も何時間にもわたって教育訓練を受けているようなもの」とマクガワンは言う。「これまでにミスを犯したすべての患者について，私はどんな細かなことも話すことができる。人命を軽んじる人がいるなんて，人の命をとても大切にしている私にとって耐えられないことだ」。

「モラルインジャリー（道徳的負傷）」とは良心に大きく反する状況や，自身の核となる価値観を脅かす状況に直面したときに生じる特別なトラウマを指す。この問題に苦しむマクガワンのような人々は，罪悪感や怒り，そして自分自身や他者を許せないという痛切な感覚に苛まれる。

モラルインジャリーは様々な場で社会的使命を担う何百万人もの人々にかかわる問題だ。医療資源が限られた環境下で，医師は少数の患者しか診られず，多くの患者を門前払いにしなければならない。兵士は与えられた任務を完遂するため一般市民を犠牲にせざるを得ない。獣医師は引き取り手がない動物を処分しなければならない。

このトラウマは多くの人が思っているよりはるかに広がっていて深刻だ。「実際にこうしたことがあちこちで起こっているのは明白だ」と非営利団体（NPO）「モラルインジャリー・オブ・ヘルスケア」（ペンシルベニア州カーライル）の共同創設者で代表を務める精神科医のディーン（Wendy Dean）は言う。「例えばソーシャルワーカーや教育者，弁護士といった職種だ」。米国での調査によると，幼稚園から高校までの教師など教育専門職の半数以上が程度の差はあれ，道徳的に傷つく状況に直面したことがあると回答している。欧州での同様の調査では，医師の約半数が，モラルインジャリーを引き起こしかねない出来事に遭遇していたことが示されている。

しかし，モラルインジャリーに対する社会の認識が足りないため，この数字すら実態にそぐわないほど低いと思われる。多くの人は自分に起こっていることを言い表すぴったりした言葉を持っていない。正確な数字がどうであれ，精神衛生上の影響は甚大だ。ロンドン大学キングスカレッジが 13 件の研究についてメタ解析を行った結果，モラルインジャリーによって，うつや自殺衝動の割合が高まることが指摘された。

COVID が世界を席巻したとき，医療従事者だけでなく，現場で働く多くの人々にとって道徳的な苦悩を伴うジレンマが新たな日常となり，モラルインジャリーの危機はより切迫したものになった。店舗スタッフは生活のために自分自

この記事の読み方

moral injury は，最近医療や看護の現場で用いられつつある概念。「道徳的負傷」と訳せるが，訳文では，あえてそのまま「モラルインジャリー」としてある。これには新参の用語だという含みもあるが，英語の moral には「道徳的／倫理的」といった訳語では表現しきれないニュアンスがあるためである。moral injury は，自分ではどうにもできない出来事によって自分の倫理観が心理的・感情的に大きな傷を負うことを指す。意味的には「良心の傷」に近い。

こうした症状の存在は昔から知られていたが，「モラルインジャリー」という名称が与えられたことによって，その存在がより明確になり，本人もそれを自覚できるようになった。記事では，コロナ禍の医療場面でのモラルインジャリーの事例を紹介したうえで，類似の症候群として戦争や戦闘場面での “battle fatigued”（戦闘疲労）を挙げ，それと対比させてモラルインジャリーの特徴を紹介している。掲載文以降では，モラルインジャリーに対する効果的なカウンセリングやセラピーが論じられている。

記事の原題は “An Invisible Epidemic”。invisible は，この問題がこれまであまり注目されてこなかったこと（それには名称がなかったことも関係している）と，個人の内面の問題であるため知るのが難しいことの両方を意味している。

身や感染リスクの高い家族を危険にさらさなければならなかった。弁護士は依頼人と滅多に顔を合わせず，代理人として十分な役目を果たせなくなった。こうした状況では「どんなに一生懸命働いても，納得のいく仕事ができない状態が続いた」とカリフォルニア州公選弁護人のアンドリュース（Jenny Andrews）は言う。

モラルインジャリーは診断マニュアルにはまだ記載されていないが，うつや心的外傷後ストレス障害（PTSD）とは異なる精神的な症状であるとの一致した見解が得られつつある。こうした状況のもと，長年の道徳的トラウマから人々を解放する手助けとなる対処法が編み出されている。道徳的な葛藤を消し去ったり，葛藤をなくすように教え諭すのではなく，それと正面から向き合うように促すもので，時間をかけて回復を目指すために地域社会の支援を重視している。一例として，トラウマ治療を受ける人が，自分が与えてしまった害を償うにはどうしたらよいか，そのプランを立てる場合もある。

モラルインジャリーの研究はまだ始まったばかりだが，科学者や臨床医の意見は以下の点で一致している。治療を受けるかどうかにかかわらず，患者が直面している問題の本質を患者自身が理解することが治癒に向けた重要なステップになる。モラルインジャリーに苦しむ人は役立たずでも駄目な人間でもない。また PTSD や他の精神疾患にも当てはまらないだろう。彼らは自身が生きるよすがとしている道徳規範と現実との乖離に苦しんでいるのだ。モラルインジャリーで「問題となるのは，自分がどういう人間なのかという感覚だ」とディーンは言う。「モラルインジャリーという呼び方こそ，自分が過去 20 年間探し求めていたものだと言う人が多い」。

古代に遡る起源

「モラルインジャリー」という名称は退役軍人病院の精神科医シェイ（Jonathan Shay）によって 1990 年代に作られたが，そうした精神的な症状は何千年も前からあった。古代ギリシャの叙事詩『イーリアス』では，英雄アキレスが戦いの最中，親友パトロクロスを守り切れずに失い，そのことで自身を責め苛んだ。20 世紀に世界大戦が勃発すると，心に傷を負った帰還兵は「戦闘疲労」（戦争神経症）というレッテルを貼られるようになった。実際には，彼らの多くは砲弾の衝撃ではなく，思い出したくもない恥ずべき戦場での行為に苦しめられていたのだ。1980 年代，ネブラスカ大学医療センターの倫理学者だったジェイムトン（Andrew Jameton）は，このような道徳的な苦悩は軍事分野に限ったことではないと指摘した。彼が述べているように，そうした苦痛は「何が正しい行動かわかっていても，制約があって，そうした行動を取ることがほとんど不可能である」ために生じることが多い。

とはいえモラルインジャリーに関する本格的な研究が進んだきっかけは，ベトナムやイラク，アフガニスタンで従軍した多くの米軍兵士が帰還後に苦しんでいることだった。ボストンの退役軍人医療システムの臨床心理学者リッツ（Brett Litz）によれば，任務完了後のカウンセリングによってもこうした葛藤を解消できなかった退役軍人はかなり多い。彼らは戦地での民間人殺害など，自分が犯した行為によって生じた悲嘆の沼から抜け出せないでいるようだった。そうした彼らを見て，リッツは一人のセラピストを思い出した。そのセラピストは妙によそよそしく，心ここにあらずといったふうだった。後にリッツはその理由を知った。「それはおそらく，私と彼が会う数カ月前の出来事のせいだった。彼が車のドアを開けた時，ちょうど自転車で走ってきた子どもがそのドアにぶつかって死んでしまったのだ」とリッツは言う。「彼は心が壊れ，私はそうした心の状態の人間を目の当たりにしたのだった」。

リッツは退役軍人と長く話しているうちに，これは PTSD やうつとは異なる様態だと確信するようになった。PTSD は通常，生命や安全が脅かされる出来事が原因となっている。これに対し，退役軍人たちに見られる長引くトラウマの多くは，個人への直接的な脅威とは関係がなかった。それは積み重なる罪悪感と絶望感，つまりは「非人間性と意味の欠如，グロテスクな戦争行為への参加といったものの総体」と関連していると彼は言う。「彼らは社会ののけ者だった。少なくとも本人たちはそのように感じていた」。

リッツは，シェイの先行研究をもとにモラルインジャリーの概念を確立し，研究者たちがこれを深く研究して，最善の治療法を考え出せるようにしようと決意した。「モラルインジャリーは私たちの文化に影響を与え，広範囲に波及することになるだろう，と私は考えた」と話す。「だから科学の力を駆使する必要があり，それには用語をきちんと定義しなければならなかった」。

リッツらは2009年にモラルインジャリーに関する包括的な論文を発表した。退役軍人たちが直面している共通の道徳的な苦悩を概説し，犯してしまったことに対して償いをして，そこに本人が意味を見いだすという治療法を提案した。また彼は「モラルインジャリーを引き起こす可能性のある出来事」のすべてがモラルインジャリーをもたらすわけではないとも述べている。もし誰かを殺したとしても，そのことが完全に正当化されると感じていれば，モラルインジャリーは生じないかもしれない。モラルインジャリーは，世界は基本的に公正で善良であると考えていたのに，自分のしたことや目撃したことによって，そうした考えが打ち砕かれてしまったときに引き起こされる傾向がある。

リッツの論文はすぐ，当時スター・キング神学校（カリフォルニア州）の客員研究員だったブロック（Rita Nakashima Brock）の目にとまった。反戦活動家でもある神学者のブロックは，戦闘に加担したという道徳的影響に関して帰還兵が証言する「戦争における良心に関する真実委員会」の開催を準備していた。

ブロックの反戦運動は個人的な体験に基づいていた。米陸軍の衛生兵だった父親はベトナム戦争から帰還した後，家族と距離を置くようになった。愛する人たちと話をしているうちに，怒りが爆発するのだった。「父があまりに変わってしまったので，私はもう家にいたくなかった」と彼女は言う。父親が亡くなった後，ブロックはいとこの助けを借りて，語られなかった父の話を明らかにした。従軍中，父と一緒に働いていた若いベトナム人女性のガイドが，後に拷問を受けて殺されたのだった。何が起こったかを知った彼は恐怖におののいた。そしておそらくは，自分のガイドを務めたことが彼女を危険にさらしたことを知って罪悪感にひどく苛まれたのだろう。

リッツのモラルインジャリーの論文を読んですぐ，ブロックにはひらめくものがあった。「同僚と私はそれを読んで，『ああ，なんてこと。そういうことだったのね』と言ったの」と彼女は振り返る。「真実委員会で証言する全員に論文を送って，『これを読んで』と伝えました」。

Elizabeth Svoboda
カリフォルニア州サンノゼ在住のサイエンスライター。著書に"What Makes a Hero? The Surprising Science of Selflessness"（Current，2013）がある。

監修

鈴木光太郎（すずき こうたろう）

新潟大学名誉教授。東京大学大学院人文科学研究科博士課程中退。専門は実験心理学。著書に『増補 オオカミ少女はいなかった』（筑摩書房，2015年），『謎解き アヴェロンの野生児』（新曜社，2019年），編著に『別冊日経サイエンス255　新版 意識と感覚の脳科学』（2022年），『別冊日経サイエンス259　新版 認知科学で探る 心の成長と発達』（2023年），訳書にベリング『ヒトはなぜ自殺するのか』（化学同人，2021年），グラツィアーノ『意識はなぜ生まれたか』（白揚社，2022年），ドレガー『ガリレオの中指』（みすず書房，2022年），ベリング『なぜペニスはそんな形なのか』（DOJIN文庫，2023年）などがある。

日経サイエンスで鍛える科学英語
心理学編

2023年12月26日　　第1刷

監修者　鈴木光太郎

編　者　日経サイエンス編集部

発行者　大角浩豊

発行所　株式会社日経サイエンス
https://www.nikkei-science.com/

発　売　株式会社日経BPマーケティング
〒105-8308　東京都港区虎ノ門4-3-12

印刷・製本　株式会社シナノ パブリッシング プレス

ISBN978-4-296-11931-8

Printed in Japan